PERFECT SACRIFICE

SPRING HARVEST
PRAISE
2009

Spring
Harvest

Equipping the Church for action

Copyright & Photocopying

Acknowledgements

Music type-setting and new arrangements by David Ball
Design & Layout by Wildfire Studio
Printed in England by Halcyon

Published and distributed by Elevation, 14 Horsted Square, Uckfield, East Sussex, TN22 1QG, UK.

Part of the Memralife Group, Registered Charity number 1126997, a Company limited by guarantee, registered in England and Wales, number 6667924.

Registered Office: 14 Horsted Square, Uckfield, East Sussex. TN22 1QG

Spring Harvest wishes to acknowledge and thank the following people for their help in the compilation and production of this song book: Andreana Arganda, Leigh Barnard, Pete Broadbent, Andrew Crookall, Cheryl Jenkinson, Trevor Michael, David Peacock, Sue Rinaldi, Rachel Whitney and Memralife Head Office staff.

Thank you to Marie Birkinshaw, Nick Harding, Sam Hargreaves, Chrissie Kelly, Gerard Kelly, Ben Langeveld, John Leach and Martin E Leckebusch for liturgy contributions.

ISBN 978-1-899788-66-8

CONTENTS

Songs are listed in the order of first line, not title.
In a few cases, alphabetical ordering of songs has
been changed slightly, in order to ensure that page
turns are not needed in any two-page songs.

Without the Spirit...
Article by Tim Hughes

Worship is a Journey
Article by Graham Kendrick

Leading Worship with Children – Nick Drake
All Age Worship – Simon Parry
Choosing a Guitar for Worship – Dan Boreham

*The words edition of this songbook is
also available in Braille and Giant print*

INDEX

Song titles differing from first lines are in italics

A thousand times
(From the inside out)

Joel Houston

1.

Steadily

-ing, your glo-ry goes be-yond all fame. And the cry— of my heart— is to bring—

— you praise, from the in - side out. Lord, my soul— cries out. E-ver-last -

— cries out. From the in - side out. Lord, my soul— cries out, Lord.—

2.

All creation is a song
(Creation's King)

Paul Baloche
& Graham Kendrick

1. All cre-a-tion is a song, wait-ing to be sung.
2. All the na-tions are a song, wait-ing to be sung.

All of na-ture like a prayer wait-ing for a tongue.
Ev-'ry in-stru-ment and voice cre-a-ted for the One,

For who will give it voice and make its an-them ring,
the ma-ker of all things, the ma-je-sty a-bove

or rise to lead a choir of all cre-a-ted things?
who bought us back from death, with such a cost-ly love:

Lord, hear your peo-ple sing. Bless-ing, ho-nour,
what praise could be e-nough?

This song is recorded on the Spring Harvest 'Live Worship 2006 - One God' and 'Songs For The King' albums

3.   All creatures of our God and King

LAAST USN ERFEUEN

Capo 1(D)

Melody from *Geistlich Kirchengessang*
Cologne, 1623
Arr. R Vaughan Williams (1872-1958)
Words: Francis of Assisi (1182-1226)
Tr. William Henry Draper (1855-1933)

1. All   crea-tures of our God and   King,   lift   up   your voice and with   us
2. Thou rush-ing wind that art so strong,   ye   clouds that sail in heav'n a-
3. Thou flow-ing wa-ter, pure and clear,   make   mu-sic for thy Lord to
4. And   all ye men of ten-der heart,   for - giv-ing oth-ers, take your
5. Let   all things their Cre-a-tor bless,   and   wor-ship him in hum-ble-

sing: Hal - le - lu - jah, hal-le - lu - jah!   Thou
long,   O   praise him, hal-le - lu - jah!   Thou
hear,   hal-le - lu - jah, hal-le - lu - jah!   Thou
part,   O   sing ye, hal-le - lu - jah!   Ye
ness,   O   praise him, hal-le - lu - jah!   Praise,

burn-ing sun with gold-en   beam,   thou   sil-ver moon with soft-er
ris-ing morn, in praise re - joice,   ye   lights of eve-ning, find a
fire so ma-ster-ful and bright,   that   giv-eth man both warmth and
who long pain and sor-row bear,   praise   God and on him cast your
praise the Fa-ther, praise the Son,   and   praise the Spi-rit, Three-in-

This song is recorded on the Spring Harvest Live Worship 'One Hope' album

gleam:
voice:
light:
care:
One:

O— praise him, O— praise him, hal-le-

lu – jah, hal-le-lu – jah, hal-le-lu – jah!

ALL THAT I AM PRAYER

Lord, let all that I am
Respond to all you are.
In our response
Jesus you are here.
You Join us, human as we are,
In our praise of the Father.
As we put our trust in Him;
As we remind ourselves of who He is;
You are here,
Showing us the perfect character of
God.
Lord, let all that I am
Respond to all you are.

All that you are:
God of the broken and the weary;
Friend of the fatherless; humble king;
Hope in hopeless places;
Light where darkness reigns;
Freedom from every captivity;
Balm to every wound.
Lord, let all that I am
Respond to all you are.

All that I am.
My strength and my weakness.
My wisdom and my foolishness
My joy and my sadness
My head and my heart
My hands and my feet
Lord, let all that I am
Respond to all you are.

4.
All I am, I lay it down

Capo 3(G)

Adam Howard

Flowing ♩ = 95

All I am, I lay it down for you, my God and friend;
Search my heart and you will find will-ing-ness to serve,

take my life in-to your hands, here I am to send.
for your cross has co-vered me with grace I don't de-serve.

O_____ Lord, lead me____ on.____

O_____ Lord, lead me____ on.____

Words & Music: © Adam Howard/RESOUNDworship.org, Adm. The Jubilate Group
4 Thorne Park Road, Torquay TQ2 6RX, UK copyrightmanager@jubilate.co.uk   Used by permission

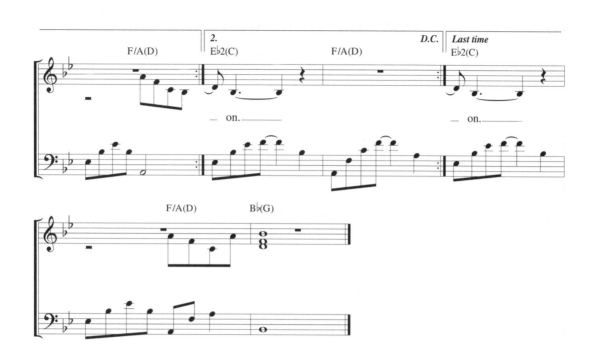

5.
All I have and all I am
(All to you)

Eoghan Heaslip
& Neil Bennetts

Capo 3(D)

Worshipfully

All I have and all I am I lay here at your feet.

Lord, I bring my ev - 'ry part here as an of - fer - ing.

Bridge

Take my will, my heart, my mind, my all; let my ev-'ry

breath be for you. *Chorus* I give my life to you my King; I sur-ren-

-der all to you. As I live my life, be glo-ri-fied. I sur-ren-

6.
All I have and all I am is yours
(Build this house)

Lou & Nathan Fellingham
& busbee

7.

Amazing grace
(My chains our gone)

Freely

Words: John Newton (1725-1807)/John P Rees (1828-1900)
& Edwin Othello Excell (1851-1921)
Arr. and additional choruses
by Chris Tomlin & Louie Giglio

Verse

1. A - maz - ing grace! how sweet the sound that
grace that taught my heart to fear, and
has pro - mised good to me, his
shall soon dis - solve like snow, the

saved a wretch like me; I once was lost, but
grace my fears re - lieved; how pre - cious did that
word my hope se - cures; he will my shield and
sun for - bear to shine. But God who called me

Last time to Coda

1st time only

now am found, was blind, but now I see. 2. 'Twas
grace ap - pear, the
por - tion be as
here be - low will

2., 3.

hour I first be - lieved.
long as life en - dures.

Chorus

My chains are gone, I've been set

This song is recorded on the Spring Harvest 'Wonderful Saviour: New Songs for 2008' album

20

free, my God, my Sa - viour has ran - somed me. And like a

flood his mer - cy reigns, un - end - ing love, a - maz - ing grace.

1.,3.   *D.C.*   *2.*   *D.S.*

3. The Lord   My chains are
4. The earth

Coda

be for - e - ver mine.

8.

At the start
(The glory of it all)

David Crowder

Capo 2(A)

24

Last chorus:
Oh, the glory of it all is you are here
For the rescue of us all that we may live.
Oh, the glory of it all. Oh, you are here
With redemption from the fall that we may live.

9.

Be still and know
(Be still)

Mark Tedder

With awe

Be still_____ and know_____ that I_____ am your God;

_____ be still,_____ be still._____ I am_____ your God._____

The na - tions know_____ your match - less name,_____ the earth
- man race_____ can - not_____ con - tain_____ the glo -

re - sounds_____ with thun - d'rous praise,_____ the rocks_____ and trees_____ de - clare
- ry from_____ your throne_____ of grace,_____ so here_____

_____ that you_____ are God._____ The hu -_____ we stand_____

10. Before the first

Capo 1(A)

♩ = 82

Kieran Metcalfe

1. Be - fore the first, be - yond the last, the e - ver reign - ing one. Age to age, the one who was, the one who is and is to come, oh Lord. So glo - ri - ous, you are
2. You hung the stars, rolled out the skies and set the earth in place. All the works your hand has made re - flect your glo - ry, sing your praise, oh Lord. So glo - ri - ous, you are
3. Yet here we stand a - mazed by grace, for, by the light of your Son. Lost are found, the weak made strong, and bro - ken hearts re - joice as one and sing: so glo - ri - ous, you are

Verse

Chorus

29

CHOOSING TO SERVE
PRAYER

(BASED ON ISAIAH 1:17)

This day, may we hear the word of the Lord,
This day, may we stop doing wrong and learn to do right,
This day, may we seek justice and help the oppressed,
This day, may we defend the cause and plead for those in need.
This day, may we choose to serve the Living Lord. Amen.

Blessed are you
(Go and shine)

Capo 2(A)

Mark Tedder

Quietly rhythmic

2. Blessed are the per - se - cu - ted, for

1. Blessed are you___ who are poor.___

theirs is the king - dom of God.___ Blessed are the false - ly ac - cus -

Blessed are you___ who mourn.___ Blessed are you___ who are meek.___

ed, they find their strength in the Lord,___ in the Lord.

Blessed are those___ who still seek right - eous - ness.

Blessed are the bro - ken in spi - rit, for

Blessed are those___ who are hun - gry.

12.
Bring heaven to earth, Lord
(We are blessed)

Capo 3 (D)

Andy Flannagan

Moderate 4

(continued over...)

Christ is the One who calls

LOVE UNKNOWN

Words: Timothy Dudley-Smith
Music: John Ireland
Arr. David Peacock

1. Christ is the One who calls, the one who loved and came, to whom by right it falls to bear the high - est Name. And still to - day our hearts are stirred to hear his word and walk his way.

2. Christ is the One who seeks, to whom our souls are known; the word of love he speaks can wake a heart of stone. For at that sound the blind can see, the slave is free, the lost are found.

3. Christ is the One who died, for - sa - ken and be - trayed; who, mocked and cru - ci - fied the price of par - don paid. Our dy - ing Lord, what grief and loss, what bit - ter cross our souls re - stored.

4. Christ is the One who rose, in glo - ry from the grave, to share his life with those whom once he died to save. He drew death's sting and broke its chains; who lives and reigns our ri - sen King.

5. Christ is the One who sends his sto - ry to de - clare, who calls his ser - vants friends and gives them news to share. His truth pro - claim in all the earth; his match - less worth and sav - ing Name.

14. Christ, the eternal Lord

Words: Timothy Dudley-Smith
Music: George Elvey
Arr. Roger Mayor

DIADEMATA

Steadily ♩ = 120

1. Christ, the e - ter - nal Lord, whose pro - mise here we claim, whose gifts of grace are free - ly — poured on all who name your Name. With thank - ful - ness and praise, we

2. Christ, the un - chang - ing Word, to ev - 'ry pass - ing age, whose time - less teach - ings still are — heard, set forth on Scrip - ture's page. Trans - form our thought and mind, en -

3. Christ, the re - deem - ing Son, who shares our hu - man birth, and by his death sal - va - tion — won for ev - 'ry child of earth. In - spire our hearts, we pray, to

4. Christ, the un - fad - ing light, of e - ver - last - ing day; our Morn - ing Star in splen - dour — bright: the Life, the Truth, the Way. That light of truth you gave, to

5. Christ, the as - cen - ded King, ex - al - ted high a - bove, whose praise, un - end - ing a - ges — sing, whom yet un - seen we love. When mor - tal life if past, your

This song is recorded on the Spring Harvest 'Songs for the King' album

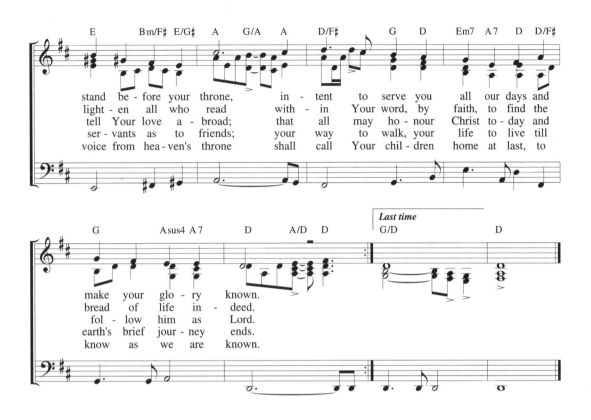

stand be - fore your throne, in - tent to serve you all our days and
light - en all who read with - in Your word, by faith, to find the
tell Your love a - broad; that all may ho - nour Christ to - day and
ser - vants as to friends; your way to walk, your life to live till
voice from hea - ven's throne shall call Your chil - dren home at last, to

Last time

make your glo - ry known.
bread of life in - deed.
fol - low him as Lord.
earth's brief jour - ney ends.
know as we are known.

MAY GOD GIVE YOU BLESSING

When you are too full to care
Too frightened to dare
Too free to be aware
When your needs are so
well met
You haven't truly felt
them yet

May God give you
The gift of hunger
And In your hunger
May He fill you

When distractions catch you
And the markets throw their
magic at you
When hawking voices

Hijack choices
And you chase the toys
You're told you'll need
Replacing deeper joys
That love might feed
When you taste the treats
that tempt
But leave you empty

May God give you
The gift of hunger
And In your hunger
May He fill you

If your heart is hollow
For want of a dream
If your soul is shallow

Your spirit, lean
If you face
Emaciation
For lack of true
Imagination

May God give you
The gift of hunger
And In your hunger
May He fill you

© **GERARD KELLY**

15.

Dance, dance
(Joy is in this place)

With a strong rhythm

Words: John Newton (1725-1807)
Music & words adaption: Tim Hughes

1. Dance,— dance,— e - v'ry-bo-dy dance, e - v'ry-bo-dy sing, for joy—
2. Shout,— shout,— e - v'ry-bo-dy shout, e - v'ry-bo-dy scream, for joy—

— is in this place now. Dance,— dance,— e - v'ry-bo-dy dance, e -
— is in this place now. Shout,— shout,— e - v'ry-bo-dy shout, e -

- v'ry-bo-dy sing, for joy— is in this place now.
- v'ry-bo-dy scream, for joy— is in this place now.

And e - v'ry-bo-dy dance now.—
Yeah, joy— is in this place now.—

This song is recorded on the Spring Harvest 'Distinctive Sounds: Glory', 'Live Worship 2006 - One God' and 'How Sweet The Sound' albums

16. Everlasting

Steadily

Sue Rinaldi
& Caroline Bonnett

1. E - ver - last - ing, e - ver true,___ all cre - a - tion___
2. Ne - ver chang - ing, awe - some___ God.___ Sing the glo - ry___

sings to you.___ E - ver faith - ful, liv - ing___ Lord,___ let the sound of
of the Lord.___ E - ver lov - ing, Ho - ly___ One,___ I will praise what

praise be heard.___ Je - sus,___ you are___ all___
you have done.___

___ that I am liv - ing for___ and all that I be - lieve is in you.___ Je - sus,___

___ all___ that I am liv - ing for,___ and all that I be - lieve is in you.

Everlasting God
(Yesterday, today and forever)

17.

Capo 3 (D)

Rock style

Vicky Beeching

1. E - ver - last - ing God,___ the years go by but you're___
2. Un - cre - a - ted One,___ you have no end and no -

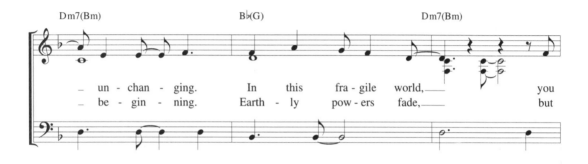

___ un - chan - ging. In this fra - gile world,___ you
___ be - gin - ning. Earth - ly pow - ers fade,___ but

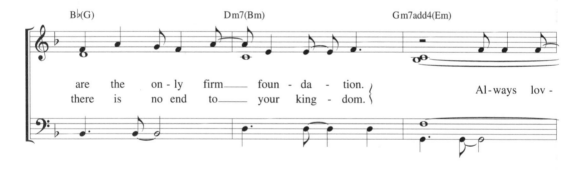

are the on - ly firm___ foun - da - tion. ⎰
there is no end to___ your king - dom. ⎱   Al - ways lov -

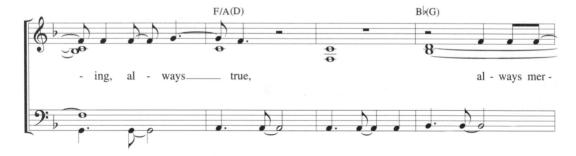

- ing, al - ways___ true, al - ways mer -

(continued over...)

18.
Everyone needs compassion
(Mighty to save)

Reuben Morgan
& Ben Fielding

Steady 4

1. Ev-'ry-one needs com-pas - sion, love that's ne-ver-fail
2. So take me as you find___ me, all my fears and fail

- ing; let mer - cy fall on___ me.___
- ures, fill my life a - gain.

Ev'ryone needs for-give - ness,___ the kind - ness of a sa-
I give___ my life to fol - low___ ev - 'ry-thing I be-

- viour; the hope of na - tions. ___
lieve in, now I sur - ren - der.___

This song is recorded on the Spring Harvest Live Worship 'One Hope' album

47

19.

Father, my heart belongs to you
(Father, I am yours)

Ballad

Luke Finch

49

20.

For every song
(You are)

Capo 2(G)

Ben Cantelon, Tim Hughes
& Nick Herbert

Steadily, with strength

51

21.

Forth in your Name
(Be glorified in me)

Words: Charles Wesley (1707-1788)
Adpt. Graham Kendrick
Music: Graham Kendrick
Arr. Henry George

1. Forth in your Name, O Lord, I go, my dai - ly la - bour to pur - sue;
2. Pre - serve me from my call - ing's snare, and hide my sim - ple heart a - bove.
3. Give me to bear your bur - den light, and ev - 'ry mo - ment watch and pray,

_ you, on - ly you, re - solve to know in all I think or speak or
_ A - bove the thorns of chok - ing care the gild - ed baits of world - ly
_ and things e - ter - nal keep in sight, and has - ten to your glo - rious

do; in your Name I go, Lord. The task your wis - dom has as - signed,
love; in your Name I go, Lord. You may I set at my right hand,
day; in your Name I go, Lord. For you de - light - ful - ly em - ploy

— oh, let me cheer-ful-ly ful-fill;— in all my works— your pre-sence find,—
—whose eyes my in-most be-ing know,—and la-bour on— at your— com-mand,
— what-e-ver boun-teous grace has giv'n;—and run my course—with stea-dy joy,—

— and prove your good and per-fect will; in your Name I go.—
— and of-fer all my works to you; in your Name I go.—
— and close-ly walk with you to heav'n; in your Name I go.—

Be glo-ri-fied— in me,— be glo-ri-fied— in me.—

In all I do,— in all I say,— Je-sus, be glo-ri-fied— in me.—

In all I do,— in all I say,— Je-sus, be glo-ri-fied— in me.—

IN THE SILENCE
OF YOUR SOUL BLESSING

In the silence of your soul
May his voice reach you
In the cracks
Where you are broken
In the pits
Where you sink low
In the tangled web of weeds
That choke your dreams
In the bitter sharp-edged stones
That pierce your feet
In your flaws and in your failings
In your fears
May you hear him

May you come to know the tone
Of his affection
And recognise the accents
Of his love
May his prose
Become your reading
And his poetry
Your song
May his marvels be the mine
Your mind is sourced in
His magnificence the spring
Your streams flow from
In your listening and in your longings
In your life
May you hear him

© GERARD KELLY

Giver of life

22

Tim Hughes

1. Gi - ver of life,— you ne - ver change,_____ all that is per - fect comes_ from you,_ your won - ders ne - ver cease.___ Not e - ven life,___ not e - ven death,___ nor a - ny pow'r_

2. Free - ly you give,— new e - v'ry - day;_____ your mer - cies will ne - ver fail,_ so great is your faith - ful - ness.___ Your love is kind,___ your love is pure,___ your love will al -

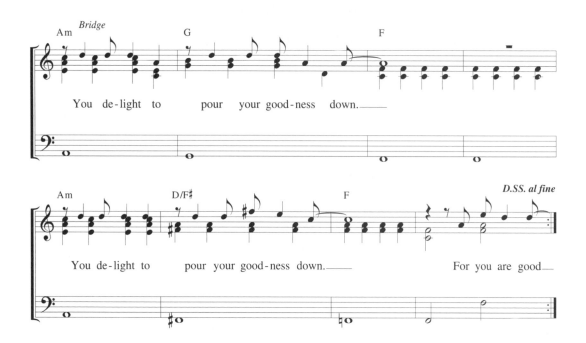

You de-light to pour your good-ness down.

You de-light to pour your good-ness down. For you are good

FOR A WORLD IN NEED
PRAYER

Lord, our world needs changed lives;
people freed from greed and compromise
people living for your kingdom, not just for themselves
Father, send us out with your gospel.

Lord, our world needs freedom;
people healed and set free,
people alive because of you.
Father, send us out with your power.

Lord, our world needs a King;
people who recognise Jesus as Son of the Living God
people who give all to follow him.
Father, send us out with your calling.

Lord, our world needs love;
people sold out for you,
and committed to each other.
Father, send us out with your compassion.

Lord, our world needs feeding;
people nourished with food and water
people fed by Word and Spirit, bread and wine.
Father, send us out with your invitation.

Lord, our world needs disciples;
**Send us out, and remain with us until the end of the age.
Amen.**

© JOHN LEACH

23.

Give unto the Lord
(Glorify the King)

Luke Finch

59

24.

God in my living
(Everything)

Tim Hughes

Capo 4(G)
Gently building

Additional choruses:
You are everything . . .
Jesus, everything . . .

25.

God of the mountains
(Creation praise)

Sue Rinaldi,
Caroline Bonnett & Steve Bassett

Moderately

1. God of the moun-tains, God of the
2. Wis-dom of a - ges, light in the

sea, God of the hea-vens,
dark, home for the out-cast,

of e - ter - ni - ty. God of the
peace for the heart: friend of the

fu-ture, God of the past,
lone - ly, strength for op - pressed,

**This song is recorded on the Spring Harvest 'One Hope: Live Worship 2008' album 'Shine - New Songs 2007'
and 'One People - Live Worship 2007' albums**

26.

Great is the Lord

Capo 4(G)

Chris Sayburn

Prayerfully

1. Great is the Lord and most worthy of praise, who can compare to his greatness? Creation displays in magnificent ways his glory, his majesty, his splendour.

2. Great is the Lord and most worthy of praise; who can determine his greatness? The heavens display in extravagant ways your glory, your majesty, your splendour.

Chorus

Great is the Father, great is the Son, great is the Spirit,

Great are you, Lord
(Awesome is the Lord most high)

27.

Fast rock

Chris Tomlin, Jesse Reeves,
Cary Pierce & Jon Abel

Verse

1. Great are you,___ Lord, migh - ty___ in strength.___
   We will praise___ you all of our days.
2. Where you send___ us, God, we will go;
   We will trust___ you when you call our name;

You are faith - ful, and
It's for your glo - ry we
you're the an - swer we
where you lead___ us, we'll

1.,3.
you will e - ver be.___
want the world to know.___

2.,4.
of - fer ev - 'ry - thing.
fol - low all___ the way.

Chorus
Raise your hands, all you na - tions, shout to
praise you to - ge - ther, for

(continued over...)

28.

Hallelujah

Capo 2(G)

Ben Cantelon

With increasing intensity

Hal - le - lu - jah, hal - le - lu - jah. You are wor - thy of our praise. Hal - le - praise. Be high and lift - ed up, be high and lift - ed up, be high and lift - ed— up,— Je - sus. It's you we glo - ri - fy, it's you we're lift - ing high. Your name be glo - ri - fied.— Hal - le -

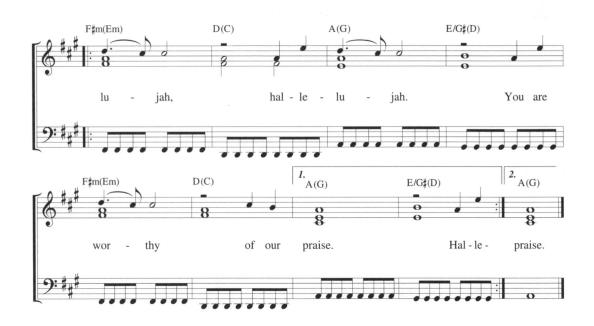

lu - jah, hal - le - lu - jah. You are wor - thy of our praise. Hal - le - praise.

WALKING WITH THE TEACHER PRAYER

(For two voices or two parts)

Walk with the Teacher, as you engage with the Scriptures,
Let his words enlighten and speak to your heart.

Walk with the Teacher, as you discover his compassion.
Let his love enfold you, bringing comfort and joy.

Walk with the Teacher, as you share in his healings,
Reflect on the journey to fulfilment and peace.

Walk with the Teacher, as you sorrow in his sufferings,
Reflect on his sacrifice that redeemed the lost world.

Walk with the Teacher, as you share in his glory,
Being part of God's Kingdom and resurrection hope.

Walk with the Teacher, as you adventure with a purpose,
Being the good news for all whom you meet.

© 2008 MARIE BIRKINSHAW

29.

He became sin
(Jesus, Messiah)

With increasing intensity

Chris Tomlin, Daniel Carson,
Ed Cash & Jesse Reeves

1. He be-came sin, who knew no sin, that
(2.) bo - dy the bread, his blood the wine,

we might be-come his right-eous - ness; he
bro - ken and poured out all for love. The

hum - bled him - self, and car - ried the cross.
whole earth trem - bled, and the veil was torn.

Love so a-ma - zing, love so a-ma - zing.
Love so a-ma - zing, love so a-ma - zing.

Je - sus, Mes - si - ah; Name a - bove all names; Bles - sed Re - deem - er; Em - man - u - el.

The res - cue for sin - ners, the ran - som from hea - ven; Je - sus, Mes - si - ah; Lord of all.

2. His All our hope

WITHOUT THE SPIRIT...
THESE THINGS ARE EMPTY

Philippians 3:3 tells us that *'we worship by the Spirit of God.'* If worship is a spiritual activity it would seem that no amount of human effort, hyping and exhortation can guarantee true worship. It is God's Spirit alone that brings life, revelation, abandonment and ultimately transformation.

On 21 August 1911, Leonardo da Vinci's 'Mona Lisa' painting was stolen from the Louvre in Paris, France. The museum was immediately closed down for an entire week as a mass operation swung into action to hunt down the missing masterpiece. When the Louvre was finally reopened, thousands of people queued up to see the blank wall space where the Mona Lisa had once hung.

It seems strange that so many people would flock to essentially see an empty space. When it comes to leading worship we can very easily get caught up with the external things - the songs, the sound levels, the lighting, and even how people are responding. The danger is we can fall into the trap of judging a successful time of worship on these things alone.

We want to pursue musical excellence and have a professional approach, but we must never lose space for the Holy Spirit to lead. We need to diligently and carefully plan and prepare all the practical elements involved in our services, but at the same time continuously remind ourselves that these things are merely the vehicle for people to engage with the Holy Spirit. Without the Spirit these things are empty.

A.W. Tozer lays down the challenge, *"If God took His Holy Spirit out of this world, what the church is doing would go right on and nobody would know the difference."* We mustn't let that happen.

Tim Hughes
Lead Worshipper

30.
Hear the call of the kingdom

Capo 3 (D)

Gospel feel ♩ = 76

Stuart Townend &
Keith and Kristyn Getty

1. Hear the

call   of   the   king-dom,   lift   your   eyes   to   the   King,——   let   his
call   of   the   king-dom   to   be   chil–dren   of   light,——   with   the
call   of   the   king-dom   to   reach   out   to   the   lost,   with   the

song   rise   with-in   you   as   a   fra-grant   of-fer-ing,   of   how
mer–cy   of   hea-ven,   the   hu–mi–li–ty   of——Christ.   Walk-ing
Fa–ther's   com–pas-sion   in   the   won-der   of   the——   cross,   bring-ing

God,   rich   in   mer-cy,   came   in   Christ   to   re–deem   all   who
just–ly   be–fore   him,   lov–ing   all   that   is   right,   that   the
peace   and   for–give-ness,   and   a   hope   yet   to   come;   let   the

This song is recorded on the Spring Harvest 'Shine - New Songs 2007' and 'One People - Live Worship 2007' albums

31.

Heaven's King

Noel Richards
& Kees Kraayenoord

79

32.

High in the heavens

Judy Gresham

♩ = 53

Verse

1. High in the hea-vens ex-al-ted, name a-bove all oth-er
2. Clothed in the splen-dour of hea-ven, Je-sus, e-ter-nal-ly
3. Let us be found in your like-ness, learn-ing to serve as you

names;— Lord o-ver all— of cre-a-tion,
God,— emp-tied your-self,— came as no-thing,
served.— Filled with your Spi-rit, your full-ness, the

wor-thy of po-wer and praise. Bles-sing and ho-nour and
choos-ing the road to the cross. Lord, you were found— in our
fra-grance of grace on the earth. You love the heart— that is

glo-ry are his e-ter-nal re-ward;
like-ness, shed-ding your glo-ry to serve;
hum-ble, you de-sire wor-ship that's true;

let ev-'ry knee bow be-fore him and ev-'ry tongue say 'he is
hum-ble, not claim-ing ad-van-tage, you laid down your life for the
voi-ces that sing for your glo-ry and lives that bring ho-nour to

Lord'.   Je - sus, you are ex-al-ted and
world.   *(Last time)* Sa - viour, all of cre-a-tion will
you.

glo - ri - fied.   Je - sus, name a-bove all names: we'll
bow in awe.   Je - sus, from ev-'ry na-tion we'll

lift you high.   high.   Lord,
call you

to the glo-ry of God,   to the glo-ry of God.

33. 'How shall they hear', who have not hear

O WALY WALY

Words: Timothy Dudley-Smith
Music: English folk tune
Arr. Dave Bainbridge, Joanne Hogg & Terl Bryant

With a slow lilt

I offer up to you
(True praises)

34.

Mark Beswick, Howard Francis
& Clive McKinley

Steadily

I of-fer up to you prai-ses from my heart, that they may be in truth the per-fect sa-cri-fice. To show my gra-ti-tude for all the things you do, I just want to give true prais-es from my heart. Lord, I give to you true prai-ses from my heart.

35.

I see the King of Glory
(Hosanna)

Brooke Fraser

Capo 2 (D)

Moderately

1.) I see the King of glory coming on the clouds with fire;
    I see His love and mercy washing over all our sin;
2.) I see a generation rising up to take their place,
    I see a near revival stirring as we pray and seek;

the whole earth shakes, the whole earth shakes.
the people sing, the people sing:
with selfless faith, with selfless faith.
we're on our knees, we're on our knees.

Ho-san-

-na, hosan-na, hosanna in the highest. Ho san-

This song is recorded on the Spring Harvest Live Worship 'One Hope' album

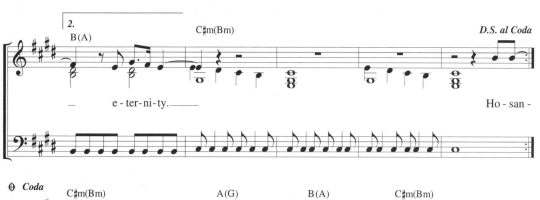

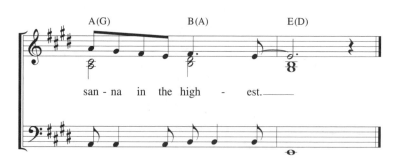

I stand amazed

36

MY SAVIOUR'S LOVE

Charles H. Gabriel (1856-1932)

Capo 1(G)
4 part harmony

1. I stand a-mazed in the pre-sence of Je-sus the Na-za-
2. For me it was in the gar-den he prayed, "Not my will, but
3. In pi-ty an-gels be-held him, and came from the world of
4. He took my sins and my sor-rows, he made them his ve-ry
5. When with the ran-somed in glo-ry his face I at last shall

rene, and won-der how he could love me, a sin-ner, con-demned, un-clean.
thine:" he had no tears for his own griefs, but sweat drops of blood for mine.
light to com-fort him in the sor-rows he bore for my soul that night.
own; he bore the bur-den of Cal-vary, and suf-fered and died a-lone.
see, 'twill be my joy through the a-ges to sing of His love for me.

Chorus

How mar-vel-lous! How won-der-ful! And my song shall ev-er be:
(O how)   (O how)

How mar-vel-lous! How won-der-ful is my Sa-viour's love for me.
(O how)   (O how)

37.

I was lost
(Grace)

Michael W. Smith
& Martin Smith

Capo 3(G)

Thoughtfully

1. I was lost—— when you found me here,—— you pulled me close,—— and—— held me near.—— And I'm a fool,—— but still you love,—— I'll be a fool—— for the King of love.——

2. There've been days—— when I've walked a-way,—— too much to car-ry, no-thing left to say.—— For-give me, Lord,—— when I'm weak and lost,—— for you trad-ed hea-ven for a wood-en cross.——

90

If ever I should falter
(With your grace)

38.

Capo 3 (G)

Martyn Layzell
& busbee

If e-ver I should fal - ter, if e ver I should fall, your love is an an - chor and a re-fuge for my soul. I build my world a - round you, I'm build - ing on the Rock, for on - ly you are faith - ful, on ly you are strong.

1. And with your grace, I can face a - no-ther day.
2. Each new day, come what may, I'm pres - sing on,

Run this race, hol - ding on - to you.
with my eyes firm - ly fixed on you.

This song is recorded on the Spring Harvest Live Worship 'One Hope' album

When all a-round me is sha - king— in this world.—

Up - on your so - lid foun - da - tion— I stand firm.——

If e - ver I— should fal-

39.

In all glory
(My God reigns)

Martin Cooper

Rhythmically

My— God reigns.

In all I do and all I say
(This is my worship)

Steadily

Nathan Fellingham

1. In all I do and all I say, let your love
   your mer - cy brings, I will work

a - bound through me. On ev - 'ry path that my life takes,
to - wards your cause. To share good news with ev - 'ry heart,

let your light shine out of me. In things that are seen,
is your charge to those you've called. Your love is so vast,

and things that are hid - den, I'll seek to de - light your heart, O God.
your grace so com - pell - ing, and all that is good is sourced in you.

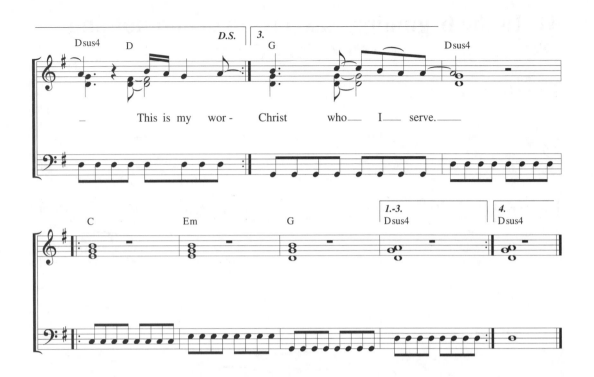

HEART, SOUL, MIND & STRENGTH
A CALL TO WORSHIP

Come to worship! Come and give God all you are!
Put your hearts into it:
make up your minds to give him the best.
With all our hearts we worship.

Open up your souls and spirits:
let his Spirit move you and touch you.
With all our souls we worship.

Don't switch off your brains:
worship thoughtfully and intelligently.
With all our minds we worship.

Put your back into it:
never tire of exalting God and showing others you mean it.
With all our strength we worship.

All creation worships God,
everything I am comes to give him the best I can.

© JOHN LEACH

41. In the beginning was darkness and nothing
(Breath of God)

Vicky Beeching

Capo 3(G)
With increasing intensity

1. In the be-ginn-ing was dark-ness and no-thing, your
2. Bones in a val-ley were changed in-to an ar-my,

Spi-rit was mo-ving o-ver the deep.
raised by your Spi-rit's po-wer-ful touch.

You spoke a whis-per and cre-a-tion ex-ist-ed,
Here in your pre-sence, I'm need-ing your re-fresh-ing;

birthed by the migh-ty words that you speak. Just say the
Lord, please re-vive my heart with your love.

set my soul a-blaze. Re-vi-val fire,_____ fall down like the rain. Re-vi-val fire,_____ set my soul a- blaze._____

D.S. al fine

In the name of the Father
(Our God saves)

Moderately

Paul Baloche
& Brenton Brown

In the name of the Fa-ther, in the name of the Son, in the name of the Spi-rit, Lord, we—— come. We're ga-thered to-ge-ther to lift up your name, to call on our Sa-viour, to fall on your grace.

In the name of the grace. Hear the joy-ful—— sound of our of-fer-ing as your saints bow—— down, as your

peo - ple— sing. We will rise with you, lift-ed on your— wings, and the

world will see—that— our God saves.———————— Our God

saves,————————— there is hope———————— in your

1st time only   2.

name.—————————— In the name of the —— Mourn-ing

turns—————————— to songs of praise;——————— our God

43. In the shadow of the cross
(*Shadow of the cross*)

Capo 2(D)

Ken Riley

Gently

44.

I've had questions
(When the tears fall)

Tim Hughes

Verse

1. I've had ques-tions with-out an-swers, I've known sor-row, I have known pain. But there's one thing, that I'll cling to; you are faith-ful, Je-sus, you're true.

2. In the lone hour of my sor-row, through the dark-est night of my soul, you sur-round me and sus-tain me; my de-fen-der, for-e-ver more.

Chorus

When hope is lost, I'll call you Sa - viour. When pain sur-rounds, I'll call you heal - er.

I'll call you Sa - viour.___ When pain sur-rounds, I'll call you heal - er.___ When si-lence falls, you'll be the song with-in my___ heart.___

TEACH US TO PRAY

As you taught your first disciples, teach us to recognise your presence and to talk with you:
Lord, teach us to pray.

Because our society and our culture need your word, may we explain the truth boldly and clearly:
Lord, teach us to speak.

When troubles surround us or engulf us, make us conscious of our security in you:
Lord, teach us to hope.

May we reflect and embody your commitment to everyone we meet day by day:
Lord, teach us to love.

Help us to use our resources wisely, placing all we have at your disposal:
Lord, teach us to give.

Show us how to invest our time and our energy in ways that will count for eternity:
Lord, teach us to live.

© MARTIN E LECKEBUSCH

Jesus Christ, you never change
(Morning Star)

Al Gordon
& Tim Hughes

1. Je - sus Christ,___ you ne - ver change, yes - ter - day, to - day the same.
2. Can you hear___ the fu - ture sound that ris - es up to shake the ground?

Morn - ing Star,___ the ris - ing sun, with you the best is yet to come.
All a - round___ the world we sing the an - them of the com - ing King.

Christ has died, Christ is ri - sen, Christ will come a - gain.
God who was, God who is, God who is to come.

Chorus

King for e - ver - more. It's you I'm___ liv - ing for, it's

⊕ Coda

Can you hear the fu - ture sound ___ ris - ing up
see the star that's break - ing through: e - ter - ni - ty is

1.
all a - round? How beau - ti - ful ___ you are. ___ We
all for you. How beau - ti - ful ___

2.
_ you ___ are. ___ Beau - ti - ful ___ you are.

46.
Jesus, there is no one like you
(How I love you)

Ben Cantelon

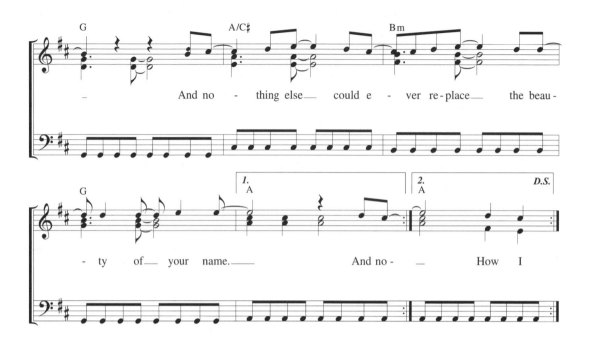

IN SILENCE, BEFORE GOD
PRAYER

In silence, before God, let us give thanks for our lives
and for everything which makes us aware of his love.

In silence, before God, let us name the challenges we face,
and ask his wisdom and strength to see them through.

In silence, before God, let us admit our worst weaknesses,
and pray for the grace of Christ to guard us from them.

In silence, before God, let us humbly acknowledge our strengths,
praying for the Spirit's gentle power to rein them in.

In silence, before God, let us name the things that frighten us,
asking for courage to confront and to defeat our fear.

In silence, before God, let us recognise our sphere of influence,
resolving to use it for Christ's purposes and his honour.

In silence, before God, let us give thanks for our lives
and renew our commitment to learn the way of Christ.

Jesus, you are here with us
(Won't stay silent)

47

Capo 3(G)

Rock

Paul Baloche, Steven Curtis-Chapman, Stuart Garrard,
Israel Houghton, Tim Hughes, Graham Kendrick,
Andy Park, Matt Redman, Martin Smith,
Michael W. Smith, Chris Tomlin, Darlene Zschech

1. Je - sus, you are here with us, our hearts are be - ing stirred.
2. Ho - ly Fa - ther, hear our cry, we're knock - ing on your door,

Spi - rit, in - ter - cede for us, with
help us Lord to per - se - vere, you

groans too deep for words. Teach us how to
know we long for more.

pray; could we be a pray'r - ful peo - ple? Shake us up to-

day, Lord. We're call - ing out,

48.

Jesus, my passion in life
(Above all else)

Vicky Beeching

Worshipfully ♩ = 82

Je - sus,——— my pas - sion in life——— is to know———
Je - sus,——— you've sho - wered your good - ness——— on

— you.—— May all o - ther goals—— bow down——— to— this
— me,——— gi - ven your gifts—— so free - ly.—— But

jour - ney of lov - ing you more.———
there's one thing I'm—— long - ing for.———

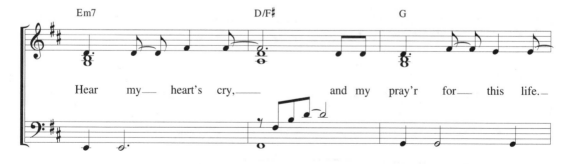

Hear my— heart's cry,——— and my pray'r for— this life.—

49.

Let voices sing
(Great Church)

Johnny and Cathy Parks
& Claire Hamilton

Steadily

1. Let voi - ces sing, let an - thems rise, the church of
   hymns de - clare his name, our hal - lowed
   hills of pow'r and peace, we stand be -

Christ has trans-formed lives! Through ge - ne - ra - tions, young and
King was with - out blame; the help - less babe, the suf - f'ring
side the poor and weak. We'll live by faith and not by

old, have served the King a - cross the globe. We join with
Christ who made him - self the high - est price. This Cor - ner -
sight; where there's dark - ness, we'll bring light. God's pur - pose

them__ in this great quest, we walk with them__ through ev - 'ry
stone__ will ne - ver shake, this Spire of Hope__ will ne - ver
since__ the dawn of time is Christ re - vealed__ to all man -

50.
Let all, all thanksgiving
(The Lord our God is one)

Graham Kendrick

Verse

1. Let all, all thanks-giv-ing be giv-en to you, our Lord. And
all earth be si-lent and know that you a-lone are

all, all that's liv-ing, be joy-ful in you, the Lord___ of all.___
God a-bove the tur-moil of na-tions, and Love has won___ the crown.___

Now, at your feet, let all the na-tions come, for the Lord, our
Wea-pons of war you'll shat-ter when you come, for the Lord, our

God, is (One.) Yes, we be-lieve,___ the Lord our God__ is One,___
God, is (One.)

This song is recorded on the Spring Harvest 'New Songs 2006/07 - Our God Reigns' album

there's no-one else,___ the high and Ho-ly One;___ so love the Lord___ with all___ your___ soul and strength: the Lord our God___ is One, the Lord our God___ is One. One.

2. Let
3. Let

O-ther gods than you have ruled___ us,

op pressed us, and con-trolled___ us. Yet, you came, and with your

blood you bought us back: now all our chains are bro- ken. all, all the

glo - ry be gi - ven to you, our Lord. To Fa - ther, Son and Spi - rit, for-

e - ver, to God, the Three—— in One.——

Life could take
(Perfect sacrifice)

51.

Lyrics: Nigel Briggs
Music: Trent

Life could take, take ev-'ry dream a-way, you'd still be my ri-sen One, the place where my hope comes from. Life could break, you'd still be my sav-ing grace, my pro-mise of all to come, the place where my hope comes from.

All my hope is in you, my trea-sure and my truth,— my hope is in you.

COMMUNION PRAYER

We remember the painful road that you walked
We share and remember
We remember the confusion of your friends
We share to remember
We remember the broken bread of your body
We share and remember
We remember the dripping wine of your blood
We share and remember
We remember who you did it all for
We share and remember

52.

Light of the World
(Here I am to worship)

Capo 2(D)

With feeling

Tim Hughes

Verse

1. Light of the World, you stepped down in-to dark - ness,
2. King of all days, oh so high - ly ex - al - ted,

o - pened my eyes, let me see beau - ty that made this
glo - ri - ous in heav'n a - bove; hum - bly you came to the

heart a - dore you, hope of a life spent with you.
earth you cre - a - ted, all for love's sake be - came

Chorus

So here I am to wor - ship, here I am to bow down, here I am to

say that you're my God, _____ and you're al - to - ge - ther love - ly, al - to - ge - ther

wor - thy, al - to - ge - ther won - der - ful to me. _____

And I'll ne - ver know _____ how much _____ it cost _____ to see _____

my sin _____ up - on _____ that cross. _____ And I'll ne - _____ that cross. _____

So here I am to

131

53.
Looking in the sky
(Amazing God)

Nathan Fellingham
& Paul Oakley

Capo 2(D)

Flowing

133

54.

Lord of the church

Capo 3(D)

Gareth Robinson

Lilting

1. Lord of the church, have your way a-mong us, Je-sus, we meet in your
2. Lord of cre-a-tion, the earth and the hea-vens, there is no oth-er like

name. We wel-come you here by your Ho-ly Spi-rit; we
you. You're awe-some in po-wer and you reign with love, in

hum-ble our-selves and pray. Bring heal-ing, for-give-ness, com-
Christ you make all things new. You heal us, for-give us, re-

pas-sion and mer-cy, be faith-ful to all of your ways. Lord, as we
deem us in mer-cy, you're faith-ful to all of your ways.

(Men)

Lord, I lift your name on high

Rick Founds

Steadily / Verse

Lord, I lift your name on high; Lord I love to sing your prais- es. I'm so glad you're in my life; I'm so glad you came to save us.

Chorus

You came from heav- en to earth to show the way, from the earth to the cross, my debt to pay, from the cross to the grave, from the grave to the sky, Lord, I lift your name on high.

This song is recorded on the Spring Harvest Live Worship 'One Hope' album

Lord, you are good

Israel Houghton

This song is recorded on the Spring Harvest Live Worship 'One Hope' album

For who you are, for who you are,

and you are good.

WHAT CAN YOU DO WITH ME, LORD? PRAYER

Jacob was a cheat, but you made him father of a nation;
Moses was a murderer, but you sent him to lead the Exodus;
Jonah was a coward, but you appointed him your messenger;
What can you do with me, Lord?

Hannah was distraught with barrenness, but you gave her children;
Esther was an orphan, but you used her to save all her people;
Ruth was an immigrant, but you made her an ancestor of kings;
What can you do with me, Lord?

Simon was weak and fickle, but you turned him into a solid rock;
Paul was the church's enemy, but you called him to missionary service;
Luke was a doctor, but you used him to write your story;
What can you do with me, Lord?

© MARTIN E LECKEBUSCH

57.
Love that will not let me go
(All that I need)

Helen Gallagher

Verse

1. Love that will not let me go, I find my rest in you
2. Love that heals my bro-ken-ness, dries my tears and mends

— a - lone: I wait for you, here I wait for you.
— my heart: I wait for you, here I wait for you.

Love that fills my heart with peace, that calls the storm in me
Love that fills my heart with song, held by you now I'll

— to cease: I wait for you, here I wait for you.
— be strong: I wait for you, here I wait for you.

Chorus

In you I find all that I need. In you I am com-plete;

58. Loved before the dawn of time
(Salvation's song)

Stuart Townend
& Andrew Small

Capo 4(G)

Steadily

1. Loved be-fore the dawn of time, cho-sen by my Ma-ker, hid-den in my Sa-viour: I am his and he is mine, che-rished for e-ter-ni-ty.
2. When I'm stained with guilt and sin, he is there to lift me, heal me and for-give me; gives me strength to stand a-gain, stron-ger than I was be-fore.
3. All the chains of Sa-tan's curse lif-ted through his of-f'ring, sa-tis-fied through suf-f'ring; all the bless-ings he de-serves poured on my un-wor-thy soul.
4. Stars will fade and moun-tains fall; Christ will shine for-e-ver, love's un-fad-ing splen-dour. Earth and heav'n will bow in awe, join-ing in sal-va-tion's song.

So with ev-'ry breath that I am gi-ven I will sing sal-va-tion's

59. Mercy to the broken hearted
(Everything changes)

Capo 1 (D)

Mildred Rainey
& Kathryn Scott

(continued over...)

145

My life is built on your promises
(Alive)

60.

Driving

Ken Riley
& Tim Hughes

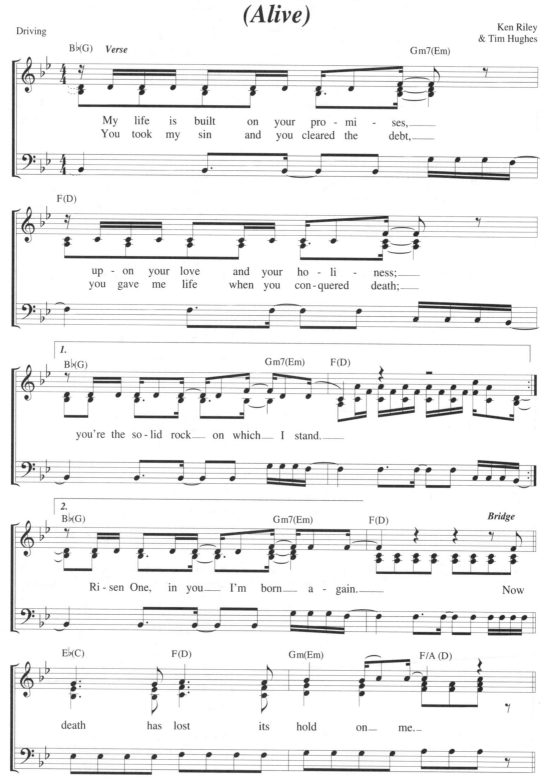

My life is built on your pro-mi-ses,
You took my sin and you cleared the debt,

up-on your love and your ho-li-ness;
you gave me life when you con-quered death;

1.
you're the so-lid rock on which I stand.

2.
Ri-sen One, in you I'm born a-gain. Now

Bridge

death has lost its hold on me.

61.
My soul will sing
(Psalm 103)

With a rock feel

Kristyn Getty
& Stuart Townend

1. My soul will sing with all the strength I
   lights to show com-pas-sion
   dust, a mo-ment in e-

have in me; I will re-joice with ev-'ry day he
to the weak; their deep-est needs he loves to sa-tis-
ter-ni-ty, as flow-ers bloom to-day and then are

gives. I will re-call the won-ders he has
fy. Through-out the earth his jus-tice and his
gone, he crowns our lives with beau-ty and with

shown to me, his pow'r to heal, his mer-cy to for-
mer-cy speak, and he will run to meet the vic-tim's
dig-ni-ty; his pa-tience smiles on all who turn to

151

wide, how high is your un-fail-ing love.

2. Our King— de -
3. Though we— are

(love.)

(Fine)

My times are in your hands
(I will hold on)

62.

Nigel Briggs

This song is recorded on the Spring Harvest albums 'Distinctive Sounds: Glory' and 'How Sweet The Sound'

63.
O Christ the same, through all our story's pages

LONDONDERRY AIR

Words: Timothy Dudley-Smith
Music: Irish traditional melody
Arr. Christopher Norton

King of all the a - ges,_____ Un - chang - ing still, a - mid the pass - ing
on your bo - dy bear - ing_____ the marks of love, in tri - umph glo - ri -
wak - ing and our sleep - ing,_____ our calm and storm, our plea - sure and our

years._____ O liv - ing Word, the source of all cre - a - tion,_____
fied._____ O Son of Man, who stepped for us from hea - ven,_____
pain._____ O Lord of love, for all our joys and sor - rows;_____

_ who spread the skies, and set the stars a - blaze._____ O Christ the
_ O Prince of life, in all your sav - ing power,_____ O Christ the
_ for all our hopes, when earth shall fade and flee._____ O Christ the

same, who wrought our whole sal - va - tion,_____ we bring our
same, to whom our hearts are gi - ven,_____ we bring our
same, be - yond our brief to - mor - rows;_____ we bring our

thanks for all our yes - ter - days.
thanks for this the pre - sent hour.
thanks for all that is_____ to be.

2. O Christ the
3. O Christ the

O Lord, you've searched me
(At the cross)

64.

Reuben Morgan
& Darlene Zschech

Capo 2(D)

Steady 4

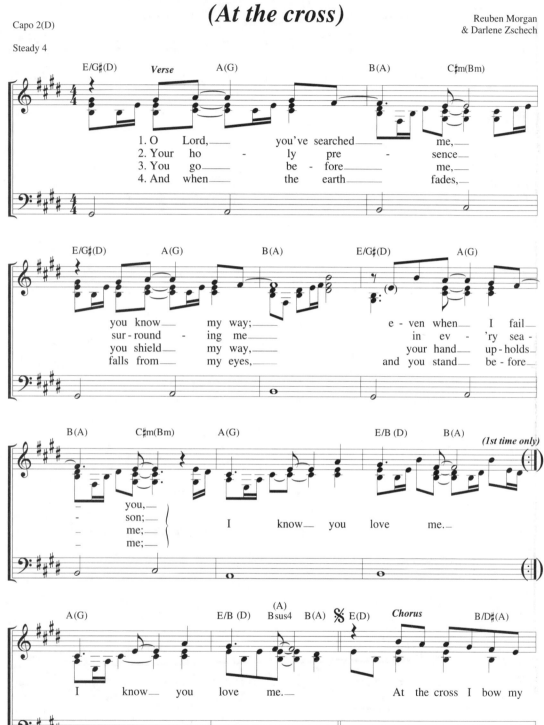

1. O Lord, you've searched me,
2. Your ho-ly pre-sence
3. You go be-fore me,
4. And when the earth fades,

you know my way; even when I fail
sur-round-ing me in ev-'ry sea-
you shield my way, your hand up-holds
falls from my eyes, and you stand be-fore

you,
son;
me;
me;

I know you love me.

I know you love me.

At the cross I bow my

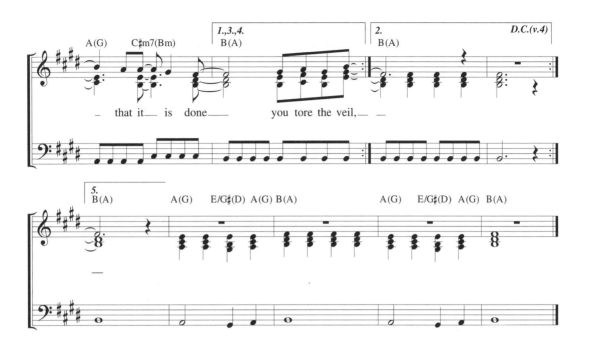

that it— is done—— you tore the veil,— —

LEARNING AND DOING
PRAYER

Yesterday has been and gone.
Some of what we did was good,
and furthered the work of Christ.
For what we did that was wrong,
we ask God's forgiveness and
receive his mercy.

Tomorrow has not arrived; it may
not be ours at all.
We cannot know all that it will
bring, good or bad, opportunities
or difficulties;
Christ tells us not to worry about it.

Today is all we have:
let us resolve to walk in the Spirit,
sensitive to his leading and
obedient to his commands.
Let us aim, today, to grow in faith,
hope and love, in worship and in
service.

**Eternal God, Father, Son and
Holy Spirit,
guide us today in our walk
with you;
let us live as disciples should,
learning and doing, learning
and doing, day by day. Amen.**

65.

O precious sight
(The wonder of the cross)

Capo 1(G)

Steadily

Vicky Beeching

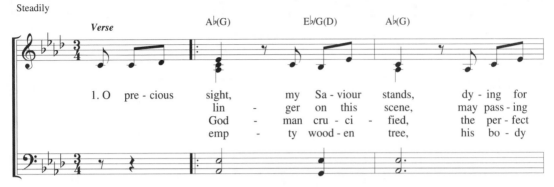

1. O pre-cious sight, my Sa-viour stands, dy-ing for
   lin - ger on this scene, may pass-ing
   God - man cru-ci - fied, the per-fect
   emp - ty wood-en tree, his bo-dy

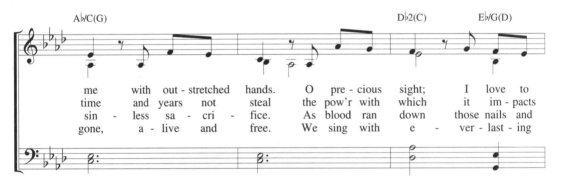

me with out-stretched hands. O pre-cious sight; I love to
time and years not steal the pow'r with which it im-pacts
sin - less sa-cri - fice. As blood ran down those nails and
gone, a - live and free. We sing with e - ver-last-ing

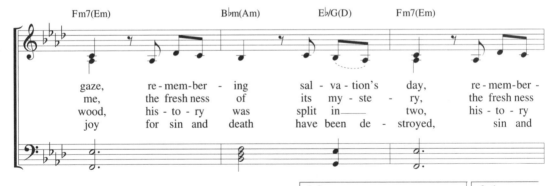

gaze, re-mem-ber - ing sal - va-tion's day, re-mem-ber -
me, the fresh ness of its my-ste - ry, the fresh ness
wood, his-to - ry was split in two, his-to - ry
joy for sin and death have been de - stroyed, sin and

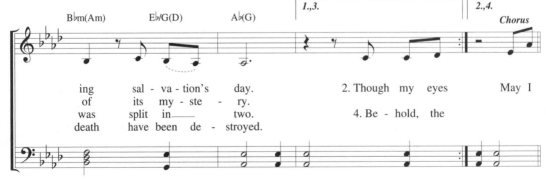

1.,3.   *2.,4.*

Chorus

ing sal - va-tion's day.   2. Though my eyes   May I
of its my-ste - ry.   4. Be - hold, the
was split in two.
death have been de - stroyed.

ne - ver lose the won-der, the won-der of the cross. May I see it like the

first time, stand ing as a sin - ner lost. Un-done by mer - cy and left

speech - less, watch ing wide - eyed at the cost.___ May I ne - ver lose the

(Fine)

won - der, the won - der of the cross. 3. Be - hold, the

D.C. al fine

163

66.
O sovereign God
(Praise the Father, praise the Son)

Ed Cash
& Chris Tomlin

Slowly

1. O sov-'reign— God, O match-less King: the saints a-
   ings, this pass-ing tide, un-der your
   val-ley, for my soul; thy great de-

dore, the an-gels sing, and fall be-fore the throne of
wings I will a-bide, and ev-'ry e-ne-my shall
scent has made me whole! Your word my heart has wel-comed

grace. To you be-longs the high-est praise.
flee; you are my hope and vic-to-
home; now peace like wa-ter e-ver

1st time only 2.,3.

2. These suf-fer-

-ry. (flows.) (So) Praise the Fa-ther, praise the Son, praise the

Chorus

Spi-rit, three in one; clothed in pow-er and in grace, the name a-

Last time to Coda

67.
On the darkest day of all

Matt Osgood

Capo 1(G)

Moderately

1. On the dark-est day of all, the Light of all the world was

crowned with thorns and lift-ed on a cross. For - sa-ken and a -

lone, the Son be-came our___ sin, sur-ren-der-ing his life for love of

us. 2. Then the dark-ness of the tomb was
dark - ness of this world, the

live   in   him,   for   we   share   his   re - sur - rec - tion   life.

1.,3.   *D.S.*   *2.*
(Fine)

3. In the   Al - le - lu - ia,   al - le -

Fm(Em)   *Db(C)*   *Ebsus4(D)*   *1.-3.*   *4.   D.S.S. al Fine*
Eb(D)   *Eb(D)*

lu - ia,   Je - sus   is   a - live!   Christ was

PERFECT PRAISE PARTNERS

Spring Harvest
Equipping the Church for action

Save on the latest Spring Harvest music resources with:

EssentialChristian.com

Featuring the top 20 new songs from this year's Praise Music book, Perfect Sacrifice will show you just how good these key songs can sound. It features two CDs, one with full band arrangements, the other stripped down and acoustic, so whether you're in a large or small church worship band, this CD is an excellent resource and source of inspiration!

Visit EssentialChristian.com now for the best deals on these and many other great Spring Harvest resources!

Available from July 09, Journey features the best of Big Top worship from Spring Harvest 2009 in a double CD collection. Featuring Graham Kendrick, Tim Hughes & Al Gordon, Vicky Beeching, Ben Cantelon, Mark Beswick and Mark Tedder, and with more songs from each Spring Harvest week than ever before, this is the definitive live worship experience. Includes many songs from the Praise 09/10 music book.

68. Once for all

Helen Gallagher

GOD STAYS THE SAME
PRAYER

Fashions fade,
favourites are erased,
A-listers evaporate;
God stays the same.

Machines rust,
innovation turns to dust,
computers crash:
God stays the same.

Politicians U-turn,
new solutions crash and burn,
headlines become
yesterdays news;
God stays the same.

Friends forget,
lovers cause regret,
families fail:
God stays the same.

Who was?
Who is?
Who is to come?
Jesus stays the same.

69.
Our God will reign forever
(My Saviour lives)

Ross Parsley

With energy ♩ = 136

1. Our God will reign for-e-ver, and all the world will know his name; ev-'ry-one to-ge-ther sing the song of the re-deemed.

2. The King has come from hea-ven, and dark-ness trem-bles at his name; vic-to-ry for-e-ver is the song of the re-deemed.

Chorus

I know that my Re-deem-er lives, and now I stand on what he did: my Sa-viour, my Sa-viour lives.

Ev - 'ry day a brand new chance to say:

'Je - sus, you are the on - ly way'. My Sa - viour,

my Sa - viour lives.

My Sa - viour lives, my Sa - viour

lives, my Sa - viour lives

70. Praise awaits for thee

Noel Robinson
& Donna Akodu

Praise a-waits for thee in Zi-on, praise a-waits for thee.

With our hearts we wel - come your pre - sence, with our mouths con - fess you are Lord.

En - ter through the gates to the courts of praise with a joy-ful sound.

71.

Praise is rising
(Hosanna)

Paul Baloche
& Brenton Brown

With strength

1. Praise is ris - ing, eyes are turn - ing to you,
   Hope is stir - ring, hearts are yearn - ing for you,

2. Hear the sound of hearts re - turn - ing to you,
   In your king - dom bro - ken lives are made new,

we turn to you.
we long for you.
we turn to you.
you make us new.

When we see you, we find strength to face the day;

in your pre - sence all our fears

72.
Praise the Lord from the heavens
(Psalm 148)

Capo 3 (D)
Steady 3

Graham Kendrick

1. Praise the Lord, from the hea - vens, praise him from the skies. Praise the Lord, hosts of an - gels, sing ce - les - tial choirs. Praise him sun and moon, praise him shin - ing stars, clouds that ride on the wind: let e - v'ry - thing with

Lord, earth and o - ceans, crea - tures of the deep. Fire and hail, ice and hur - ri - cane, let the thun - der speak. Beasts of fo - rest, field and de - sert, e - v'ry bird in the sky: from least of all to

all praise the one name wor - thy of all praise. On - ly God, our Cre - a - tor from e - ter - nal days. All his ex - cel - lence far out - shin - ing, all the worlds he has made: yet comes to us, de -

This song is recorded on the Spring Harvest 'New Songs 2004/05', 'Live Worship 2004', 'Live Worship 2005' and 'Songs For The King' albums

Last time to Coda

life and breath_____ prai - ses sing.
great - est king,_____ sing for joy.
li - vers us,_____ give him praise.

2. Praise the   To the Lord of all cre - a - tion,
3. Let them   To the Lord of all cre - a - tion,
                      Praise the Lord of all cre - a - tion,

glo - ry and ma - je - sty for - e - ver.   e - ver._____ All his
glo - ry and ma - je - sty for - e - ver.
glo - ry and ma - je - sty for

Coda

praise.

179

73.

Rock of ages

Andrew & Wendy Rayner

Rhythmic celtic feel

1. Rock of a - ges, our cre - a - tor, source of life and Lord of
2. Rock of a - ges, our sal - va - tion, bought for us up - on the
3. Rock of a - ges, God e - ter - nal, Sov - 'reign, e - ver - last - ing

all. Word of God, all things su - stain - ing;
cross. Bound - less grace so free - ly gi - ven;
Lord. Ru - ler of our fu - ture sea - sons,

Chorus

stead - fast and for e - ver sure.
vic - t'ry won at pre - cious cost. Christ our rock and firm foun -
full as - su - rance e - ver more.

da - tion, we will trust in you a - lone. One true hope for ev - 'ry

1.,2.   *3.*

na - tion; held se - cure in hea - ven's throne. throne.

WORSHIP IS A JOURNEY

If I began a service by asking you to repeat after me: 'My father was a wandering Aramean and he went down into Egypt with a few people and lived there and became a great nation', you could be forgiven for looking at me a little strangely. Yet thus begins a foundational text of Hebrew worship 'liturgy' **Deut 26:5-9**. It roots the story of their history with God in real events, in people and places, in what happened and why, locates the worshiper in the flow of a continuing story, and anticipates a destination as yet un-reached.

At the core of Old Testament worship is the retelling of 'salvation journeys', like the exodus from Egypt and return from exile in Babylon. The first recorded praise and worship song in the Bible is a kind of epic poem by Moses; and Miriam adapted part of it into a chorus with dance moves see **Exodus 15**!

New Testament worship took a similar form, using scriptures like these that compressed the events of Christ's coming into creed-like statements:

'Christ died for our sins according to the scriptures, that he was buried, that he was raised on the third day according to the scriptures.' **1 Cor 15:3-4**

'He appeared in a body, was vindicated by the Spirit, was seen by angels, was preached among the nations, was believed on in the world, was taken up in glory.' **1 Tim 3:16**

The famous words from **Phil 2:6-11** which begin: 'Christ Jesus: Who, being in very nature God, did not consider equality with God something to be grasped, but made himself nothing, taking the very nature of a servant…' are believed by many to have been the lyrics of an early church hymn. Like our ancient creeds, they describe an unfolding of an incredible event.

When we share in the bread and wine, we are taken on a sensory journey, of touch, taste, smell, sight and hearing, into a kind of reconstruction of that ancient meal, re-enacting the historical events that make relationship with God possible. By faith we re-enter the story and meet the risen Christ anew.

In my view one of the dangers we face today is the loss of 'journey' and 'story' in worship.

For many churches, the word worship has become synonymous with singing, and if the singing only tells of the present moment, or subjective experience, or is a random collection of songs strung together merely by associations of tempo, key and mood, with no cohesive content, then it can become as one commentator put it: *'a shapeless searching after God that never arrives at it's destination'* **Derek Tidball**.

Robert Webber says that: *'worship is not a programme of isolated acts of worship. It is a narrative. A retelling of the story of our relationship with God in history, past and present,'*

Isaiah's vision of God's throne in **Isaiah 6** is seen by many as a pattern for the worship journey, from a revelation of God's holiness, to the recognition of sin, to rescue by God's own sacrifice, to hearing God's call to serve, to responding and being sent out. That's quite a journey!

Look at scriptures like **Psalm 95**, **Rev 5: 6-14**, **Heb 10: 19-25**, and you will discern similar progressions through stages of God's revelation of himself, and the worshipers response.

Journeys move us from point A to point B, with scenes and experiences along the way. Next time you plan a worship gathering, think about a journey where A is the call to worship, and B is the sending out to serve. Think about how we can use words, music, symbols and actions to retell the story of our salvation from God's perspective, how to reference the epic worship journeys of the patriarchs, prophets, apostles and believers down the millennia. Imagine the baton being handed to us in our generation, and look for ways to anticipate the future that God has promised.

A final quote [one for the road!] that is well worth pondering:

'For it is only in remembering the mysterious, unconventional and unpredictable ways of God that we can imagine them in our time.' **John David Walt, Jr.**

Graham Kendrick
Lead Worshipper

74.

See, what a morning
(Resurrection hymn)

Victoriously

Keith Getty
& Stuart Townend

1. See, what a morning, glo - rious-ly bright, with the
2. See Ma - ry weep - ing, 'Where is he laid?' As in
3. One with the Fa - ther, An - cient of Days, through the

dawn - ing of hope in Je - ru - sa - lem;
sor - row she turns from the emp - ty tomb;
Spi - rit who clothes faith with cer - tain - ty,

fold - ed the grave - clothes, tomb filled with light, as the
hears a voice speak - ing, call - ing her name; it's the
ho - nour and bles - sing, glo - ry and praise to the

an - gels an - nounce Christ is ris - en!
Ma - ster, the Lord raised to life a - gain!
King crowned with pow'r and au - tho - ri - ty!

This song is recorded on the Spring Harvest 'Live Worship 2004', 'He Is Risen', and 'Songs For The King' albums

See God's sal - va - tion— plan, wrought in love, borne in pain,— paid in
The voice that spans the— years, speak - ing life, stir - ring hope,— bring - ing
And we are raised with— him, death is dead, love has won,— Christ has

sa - cri - fice,———— ful - filled in Christ, the— man, for he
peace— to us,———— will sound till he ap - pears, for he
con - quered;———— and we shall reign with— him, for he

lives: Christ is ri - sen from the dead!————
lives, Christ is ri - sen from the dead!————
lives, Christ is ri - sen from the dead!————

75. Shout the news that God is here
(Shout it)

Latin feel

Geraldine Latty

1. Shout the news that God is here;—— let them—— know, let ev-'ry one—— know. The si-lenced voice can sing a-gain;—— let them—— know, let ev-'ry one—— know.——— Shout it - let the sky give—— voice. Shout it - let the earth ap-plaud. Shout it - let the sea make—— noise. For our God is

2. Shout the news that God is here;—— let them—— know, let ev-'ry one—— know. The ones a-ban-doned found a-gain;—— let them—— know, let ev-'ry one—— know.

3. Shout the news that God is here;—— let them—— know, let ev-'ry one—— know. The hope-less can be-lieve a-gain;—— let them—— know, let ev-'ry one—— know.

(2.)
(3.)

This song is recorded on the Spring Harvest Live Worship 'One Hope' album

with us - for the poor and the faint. With us - for the vic - tim a-fraid.
with us - for the wor - ker un-paid. With us - for the child like a slave.
with us - to be good news to-day. With us - to be com - fort in pain.

With us - for the home - less a - gain.
With us - for the land that longs for rain. } Yes, our God of love, our God is
With us - to an nounce a bet - ter way.

1.,2.

great!

To end

great!

76.

Sing unto the Lord a new song

Mark Beswick, Howard Francis
& Nicky Brown

Very rhythmic

Sing un-to the Lord — a new — song, bless — him, praise — him, lift —

— him high - er. All you cho - sen gen - er - a - tion, dance —

— and cel - e - brate. If you lift him high, he will

draw us near - er, e - ver clo - ser to — him day by — day.

If you lift him high, he will draw us near-
-er, e - ver clo - ser to— him ev - 'ry— day.

COMMISSIONING PRAYER

(BASED ON MATTHEW 28:17–20 & 10:7–8)

(said by all together)

Jesus we worship you,
And sometimes we doubt.
Yet we know all authority is yours.

So you call us to go:
    to all nations,
    to make disciples,
    to continue your mission.

You call us to announce your
Kingdom:
    to heal the sick,
    to raise the dead,
    to cast out demons.

You call us to baptise in your
name:
    you are Father,
    you are Son,
    you are Holy Spirit.

We will follow, we will obey and
teach all you have commanded,

For you are with us always,
day after day, year after year,
to the very end of the age.
Amen.

77.

Spirit of God

Steadily

Stuart Barbour

Verse G | D/G | G | C/G | F

Spi-rit of God,— fill my heart,— show me how to be like Je-

D Dsus4 D | G | D/G | G

-sus. Let no earth-ly thing— pull me a-way;—

C/G | G | D Dsus4 D | C | G

teach me how to live in your free - dom. Let your king-dom come,— your

D | G | C | G | Dsus4 D *Chorus*

will be done;— Lord, do it through— me.— I will serve the

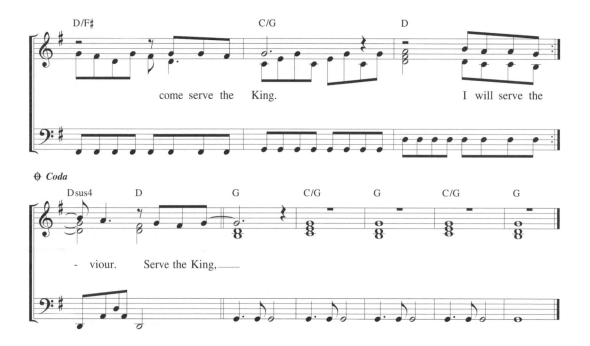

come serve the King.

I will serve the

⊖ Coda

-viour.   Serve the King,——

CREED

(BASED ON COLOSSIANS 1:15–20)

Leader
& Congregational Response

We look to Jesus and see the God who cannot be seen.
He is the image of the
invisible God.

We look to Jesus and see God's purpose for everything.
He is the first born over creation.

Everything was created through him and for him:
Everything in earth and heaven,
Everything seen and unseen,
Everything held together by him.

We look to Jesus to lead us, his Church.
He is the head, we are his body.

We look to Jesus; first in the beginning, first at the end.
He is the first born from the dead.

Everything is restored to God through him:
Everything in earth and heaven,
Everything broken and dislocated;
His death on the cross restores
everything, forever.
Amen.

78

Strength will rise
(Everlasting God)

Brenton Brown
& Ken Riley

Capo 3(G)
Moderately

Strength will rise as we wait upon the Lord, we will wait

up-on the Lord, we will wait up-on the Lord. up-on the Lord. Our God,

you reign for - e - ver. Our hope,

our strong de - li - v'rer.

You are the e - ver - last - ing God, the e -
You're the de - fen - der of the weak, you com -

79.
Sweet Jesus Christ
(Mystery)

Charlie Hall

Moderate rock

Verse

Sweet Je - sus Christ, my sa - ni - ty;
sweet Je - sus Christ, my cla - ri - ty.

Bread of hea - ven, bro - ken for me;

Cup of sal - va - tion, held out to drink.

Je - sus, my - ste - ry.

Chorus

Christ has died and Christ is

80.

Take my life
(Surrender)

Capo 2(D)

Kelly Delp
& Nathan LaGrange

81. The greatest day in history
(Happy day)

Tim Hughes
& Ben Cantelon

Steadily

1. The great-est day in hi-sto-ry, death is beat-en, you
   The emp-ty cross, the emp-ty grave, life e-ter-nal, you

2. When I stand, in that place, free at last, meet-
   End-less joy, per-fect peace, earth-ly pain fi-

— have res-cued me. Sing it out, Je-sus is a-live.
— have won the day. Shout it out, Je-sus, you are mine.
—ing face to face. I am yours, Je-sus, you are mine.
—nal-ly will cease. Ce-le-brate,

Je-sus is a-live,

he's a-live. Oh, hap-py day,

I'll ne - ver be___ the same.___

MOTHERS BLESSING

This blessing was written for Watershed Church in Charlotte, North Carolina
for Mothers Day in 2008. The church wanted to particularly honour the lives
of single mothers.

When the day is longer
Than the energy you have for it,
And the tasks you face outlast you ten
times over:
**May the rest and restoration God
Be your restorer.**

When the mouths you feed,
And the minds you mold,
And the hearts whose hopes you hold as
guarantor
Engulf you:
When the eyes whose desperation dents
your dreams
Look at and through you
**May God who sees the needs of all
who seek him
Be your shelter.**

When you dread that you don't do
enough,
And hate that you don't have enough;
When you know that you don't know
enough,
And fear that you won't be enough;

When all you can be sure of,
Is that there's something you'll need
more of:
**May God, who is beyond enough
Be your enough.**

May he who is always around you
Surround you
May he who has gone before you
Be for you
May he who is beneath and above you
Love you
**May he who invisibly holds you
Enfold you**

May you know
Beyond the boundaries of knowing
And feel
Beyond the frailty of your feelings
That you are loved
And may he who, seen or unseen, is your
kinsman
Be your redeemer

© GERARD KELLY

There is a song that must be sung
(*Round the earth*)

Tim Hughes
& Eoghan Heaslip

82.

Very rhythmic

1. ⎰ There is a — song ——
   ⎱ Our on - ly hope ——
2. ⎰ A day will — come ——
   ⎱ and there with one — heart, ——

that must be — sung,
and our on - ly — claim
in hi - sto - ry
there with one — voice,

of how grace and — love ——
is in Je - sus' name ——
when all — will — bow ——
our song — will — rise ——

have re - deemed —
we're for - gi -
down in wor -
up to - ge -

_ us
- ven,
- ship
- ther,

1.

2.
for - gi - ven.
to - ge - ther. ——

83.
There's a name I love to hear
(Blessing and honour)

Vicky Beeching

Capo 2(D)

Moderately building

1. There's a name I love to hear, Je - sus, Je - sus. It's
2. At his name the de - mons flee, Je - sus, Je - sus.

mu - sic to the sin - ner's ear, Je - sus, Je - sus.
At his name the sick are healed, Je - sus, Je - sus.

Wor - thy of the high - est praise, yours is the name by which we're
Hea - ven e - choes with your praise, join - ing their an - them now we

Chorus

saved. Bless - ing and ho - nour, glo - ry and
sing: prai - ses through - out the

pow - er be to your name, be to your name.
a - ges

84.

There's a song that's rising up
(Celebrate)

Ben Cantelon

Positively

207

This is how I know what love is

85.

Capo 4(G)

Al Gordon
& Hanif Williams

With energy

1. This is how I know what love is,————— this is how I
   This is why I come to wor-ship,————— this is why I

1.
know I'm— free, this is how I know sal-va-tion: Je-sus came and
lift my— hands,

2.
died for— me. this is why I now sur-ren-der ev-'ry-thing I am:

Chorus
Be-cause of your love;————— there's dan - cing in— my heart.—

This is my prayer in the desert
(Desert song)

86.

Moderately

Brooke Fraser

have a rea - son to wor - ship.

All I will bring

4. This is my pray'r in the har - vest, when fa - vour and pro - vi - dence

flow: I know I'm filled - to be emp - tied a - gain. The

seed I've re - ceived I will sow.

87.

This joyful Eastertide
(He is risen)

Words: George R. Woodward (1848-1934)
Adpt. Graham Kendrick
Music: Graham Kendrick
Arr. Henry George

1. This joy - ful Ea - ster - tide, a - way with sin - and sor - row; my Lord, the Cru - ci - fied, has sprung to life this mor - row.
2. Death's flood has lost its chill, since Je - sus crossed the ri - ver; Lo - ver of souls, from ill, my pass - ing soul de - li - ver.
3. My flesh in hope shall rest, and for a sea - son slum - ber; till trum - pet, east to west, shall wake the dead in num - ber.

Had Christ, that once was slain, not burst his three - day pri - son, our faith would be in vain,

88.

This is the body of Christ

John L. Bell

Gently

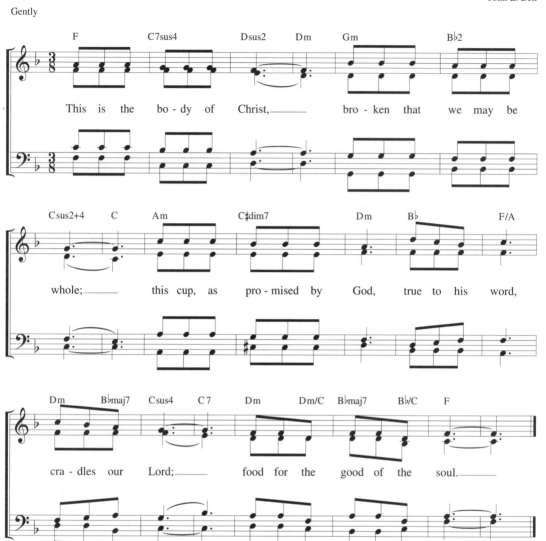

This is the bo-dy of Christ,_____ bro-ken that we may be whole;_____ this cup, as pro-mised by God, true to his word, cra-dles our Lord;_____ food for the good of the soul.____

Though trials will come
(Consider it joy)

Graham Kendrick

♩ = 65

1. Though trials will come, don't fear, don't run.
2. Though trials will come, won't fear, won't run.

Lift up your eyes, hold fast, be strong.
We'll lift up our eyes, hold fast, be strong.

Have faith, keep on be-liev - ing. Lift up your
Have faith, keep on be-liev - ing. We'll lift up our

eyes for God is at work in us,— mould-ing and
eyes for God is at
(verse 3) trust - ing him,— rea - dy for

90.

To you O Lord

Graham Kendrick

Verse

1. To you, O Lord, I lift up my soul; in you I trust,
2. Show me your ways and teach me your paths. Guide me in truth,

O my God. Do not let me be put to shame,
lead me on; for you're my God, you are my Saviour.

nor let my e-ne-mies tri-umph o-ver me.
My hope is in you each mo-ment of the day.

Chorus

No one whose hope is on you will e-ver be put to shame;

that's why my eyes are on you, O Lord. Sur-round me, de-fend me,

Veiled in humanness
(The cross speaks)

91.

Suzanne Hanna

We bow our hearts
(Adoration)

Brenton Brown

With adoration

Verse

1. We bow our hearts, we lift our hands, we
choose to leave it all behind and

turn our eyes to you again, and we surrender to
turn our eyes towards the prize. The upward call of God

the truth that all we need is found in you.
in Christ; you have our hearts, Lord; take our lives.

Chorus

Receive our adoration, Jesus, Lamb of God.

Receive our adoration; how wonderful

229

93. We could try to count the stars
(King of wonders)

Moderately

Paul Baloche, Steven Curtis-Chapman, Stuart Garrard,
Israel Houghton, Tim Hughes, Graham Kendrick,
Andy Park, Matt Redman, Martin Smith,
Michael W. Smith, Chris Tomlin, Darlene Zschech

1. We could try to count the stars; you al-rea-dy know them each by name.
2. You re-veal and we re-spond You have shown there's no one like you God;

Ev-'ry sin-gle ga-la-xy is your
your love and mer-cy wel-come us in-to

de-sign in ma-je-sty dis-played.
the beau-ty of this ho-li-ness.

Your glo-ry shines

be-fore our eyes; the more we see, the more we love

94.
We have a strong and certain hope
(I know he lives)

Graham Kendrick
Arr. Henry George

We wait in hope for you
(Unfailing love)

95.

Nigel Briggs, Rich Bull
Matt Loose & Phil Squires

Seriously

We wait in hope for you, our shel-ter and our truth.

You are al-ways faith-ful to your word.

Con-sume our hearts and minds, and be the au-thor of this life.

Your king-dom come, your will be done.

In these times of doubt and sor-row, peo-ple need a

fail - ing love.____ When the night____ crowds out the day,____ un -

fail - ing love.____ When there's no words left____ to say,____

God's love re - mains.

Coda

96.

We will sing, sing, sing
(Sing, sing, sing)

With energy

Chris Tomlin, Daniel Carson, Jesse Reeves,
Matt Gilder & Travis Nunn

Verse

1. What's not to love a-bout you? Hea - ven and earth
2. You are the love that frees us. You are the light

_ a - dore you. Kings and king - doms bow down.
_ that leads us, like a fi - re burn - ing,

Son of God, you are the One, you are the One

we're liv - ing for.

You are the One

We, your children, pray Lord
(King of the broken)

97.

Capo 1(G)

Steadily, building

Paul Baloche, Steven Curtis-Chapman, Stuart Garrard,
Israel Houghton, Tim Hughes, Graham Kendrick,
Andy Park, Matt Redman, Martin Smith,
Michael W. Smith, Chris Tomlin, Darlene Zschech

1. We, your chil - dren, pray Lord, hum - bly seek your face;
2. Heal - ing King of na - tions, let your king - dom come.
3. Lo - ver of the wound - ed, de - fen - der of the weak,

we turn from our sin, Lord, you hear
Pu - ri - fy your church, Lord, your glo -
friend of the for - got - ten; you wipe

Bridge

— us as we pray. Heal us, for - give us, re -
— ry o - ver us.
— a - way our tears.

store our hearts a - gain. Fill us, breathe up - on us.

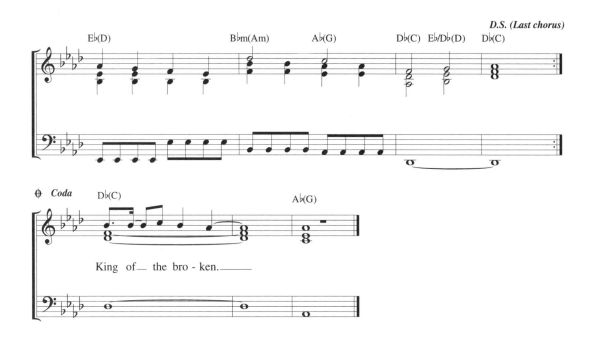

WHO DO I SAY YOU ARE?
MEDITATION

(BASED ON MATTHEW 16:13–25)

(read slowly by a single reader, or projected line by line for reflection).

Who do I say you are?
What does my life tell people about your life?
When people learn I'm a Christian,
what kind of 'Christ' do they see in me?
Where is the road that follows your footsteps?
Why do we forget that path involves suffering?
How can I lose my life,
and find it in you?

98.

We're taller when we bow
(Let us be broken)

Rhythmically

Mark Tedder, John Hartley
& Jamie Harvill

1. We're tal - ler when we bow,___ we're stron - ger when we're weak,___
rich when we are poor,___ bring hope when there is doubt;___
glo - ry is our prize,___ your pre - sence, our re - ward;___

___ we die so we can live,___ (vv.2,3) in si - lence hear you speak.
___ you e - le - vate the meek,___ hu - mi - li - ate the proud.
___ your kind - ness makes a way,___ our bro - ken - ness re - stored.

1. *2.,3.*

Bridge

___ 2. We're ___ Re - veal the hid - den pla - ces of our hearts,___

Fa - ther, and take us where___ you are.___

Let us be bro - ken, let us be bro - ken, Lord.—

Let us be bro - ken for you.— Let us be bro-

- ken, let us be bro - ken, Lord.— Let us be bro-

- ken for you.— 3. Your

245

99.
When I call on your name
(Love came down)

Capo 3(G)

Ben Cantelon

Moderate rock style

100.

When clouds veil sun
(Never let go)

Gently

Mike Hogan, David Crowder
& Mike Dodson

1. When clouds veil sun and di-sas-ter comes,
2. When clouds brought rain and di-sas-ter came,

oh, my soul, oh, my soul. When wa-ters rise
oh, my soul, oh, my soul. When wa-ters rose

and hope takes flight, oh, my soul, oh, my soul.
and hope had flown, oh, my soul, oh, my soul,

Oh, my soul. Ev - er faith-
Oh, my soul.

-ful, ev - er true. You I know, you ne-ver let go.

Coda

Oh, — what — love..

Oh, — what — love.—— Oh, — what — love.—— Joy — and pain,—

— in sun — and rain,—— you're — the same. — Oh, you - ne - ver let — go.

1.,2.

3.

— Oh, You ne - ver let — go,—— ne - ver let — go,—— ne - ver let — go.——

When I see the beauty
(What can I do)

Paul Baloche & Graham Kendrick

This song is recorded on the Spring Harvest 'New Songs 2006/07 - Our God Reigns' album

(continued over...)

D.S. al Coda

What can I

Coda

jah!

102.

When I'm Lost
(More of You)

Mark Tedder

Gently

103.

When I'm weak

Capo 43(G)

Joel Payne

Moderately ♩ = 100

Verse

1. When I'm weak,_____ you are strong, and I'm car - ried a - long__ by the po-
   - gle with sin,_____ you still wel - come me in,_____ though my heart__

   - wer of Christ__ in me._____ When I cry__ from my pain,__ you will hear__
   - should be dressed__ in shame._____ For it's Je - sus you see,__ not the sin-

   - me, and say__ that your grace_____ is e - nough__ for me._____ And for Je -
   - ner in me,__ and you clothe__ me with grace__ a - gain._____ So I will__

   - sus' sake,__ I can walk__ this way,__ if I walk__ this way__ in__ him.__
   - not fear,__ but in faith__ draw near,__ for this mer - cy is__ in__ him.__

104. When we were in the darkest night
(God of our yesterdays)

Moderately

Matt Redman

Verse

1. When we were in the dark - est night, and
   — a - head, what-

won - dered if — our eyes — would ev - er see — the light, — you were there,
e - ver roads — our grate - ful hearts — will come — to tread, you'll be there,

— Lord. When we were in — the stor - my gale, and
— Lord. And we will fix — our eyes — on you, and

won - dered if — we'd e - ver live — in peace — a - gain, you were there,
know that there — is grace — e - nough — to see — us through; you'll be there,

— Lord. You were there in the strug - gle, you were there in the fight, —
— Lord. You'll be there in the strug - gle, you'll be there in the fight, —

LOVE ME INTO LOVE
BLESSING

Love me into loving
Jesus
Grow me
Into grace
Set me up
For servanthood
Forge
Forgiveness in me
Pour me out in passion
Mould me into mercy
Caress me into caring
Lord
Recreate me
To the core

As your worship
To the father
As your love-gift
To the world
As your act
Of crafted kindness
As the music
Of your soul

Break the seals
Tip the bottle
Squeeze
The perfume out
Turn me towards tenderness
Lord
Love me into Love

© GERARD KELLY

105.

Who am I?
(Friend of God)

Michael Gungor
& Israel Houghton

Wonderful, so wonderful
(Beautiful one)

Tim Hughes

106

1. Won - der - ful, so won - der - ful is your un - fail - ing love, your
2. Po - wer - ful, so po - wer - ful, your glo - ry fills the skies, your

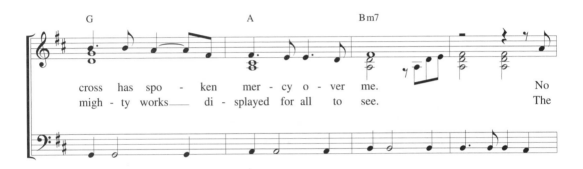

cross has spo - ken mer - cy o - ver me. No
migh - ty works di - splayed for all to see. The

eye has seen, no ear has heard, no heart could ful - ly know how
beau - ty of your ma - je - sty a - wakes my heart to sing: how

glo - ri - ous, how beau - ti - ful you are. Beau - ti - ful one I
mar - vel - lous, how won - der - ful you are.

This song is recorded on the Spring Harvest Live Worship 'One Hope' album

love you, beau-ti-ful one I a - dore, beau-ti-ful one my soul must sing.

Beau - ti - ful You o-pened my eyes— to your won - ders a-new,— you cap - tured my heart— with this love, 'cos no - thing on earth— is as beau - ti-ful— as you.— thing on earth— is as beau - ti-ful— as you.— Beau-ti-ful

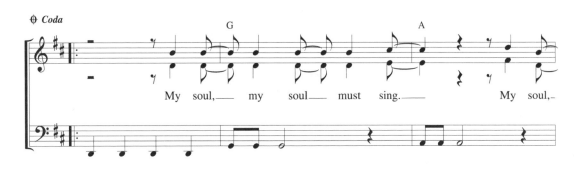

107.

Worship the Lord

Al Gordon

Steadily

Verse
G   C2

1. Wor-ship— the   Lord   in the beau-ty— of   ho-li-ness,— with awe and— with
   Lord,   in   beau-ti-ful   ho-li-ness;   lift-ing— up

Em7   C2   G

re-ve-rence,— bow to— a-dore.   You are— my   Lord,   you are— my
re-ve-rence,— I bow to— a-dore.   I give you— my   all,   sur-ren-der-ing

C2   Em7

ho-li-ness,—   Je-sus,— my   right-eous-ness,—   I   wor-ship— you,
ev-'ry-thing;—   my ev-'ry-day   of-fer-ing,—   to   wor-ship— you,

C2   **Chorus**   % G/B   C2

Lord.   I'm liv-ing for your   glo-ry,   I'm liv-ing for the

Em7   D   G/B

Name   a-bove   all— names.—   No one else is   wor-thy,

no one else can e - ver take your place.

2. I wor - ship you, You are high and— lift - ed up,

—high and— lift - ed up,— high and— lift - ed up.— You are

I'm liv - ing for your

Mid section

D.S. al Coda

⊕ *Coda*

108. Worship the Lord our God and King
(You are holy)

Stephanie Leisten

Rhythmically

1. Wor-ship the Lord, our God and King, for he is good.
2. Lift up his name in all the earth and sing his songs.

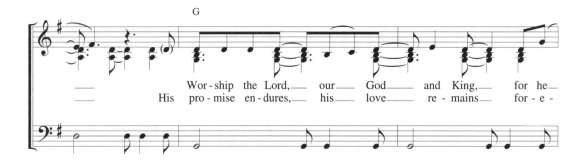

Wor-ship the Lord, our God and King, for he
His pro-mise en-dures, his love re-mains for-e-

is true. Here we come to you with our hearts
-ver-more.

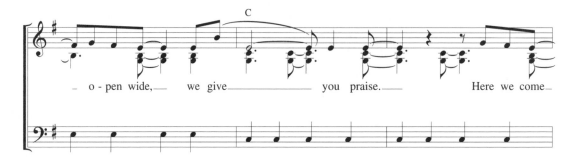

o-pen wide, we give you praise. Here we come

109

Would you restore
(Hallelujah)

Freely

Steve Fortunato

110.

You are a great God

Twila Paris

With feeling

Chorus

You are a great___ God,___ you are a great___ God,___

(Fine)   **6th time to Coda**

you are a great___ God,___ the on - ly true___ God.

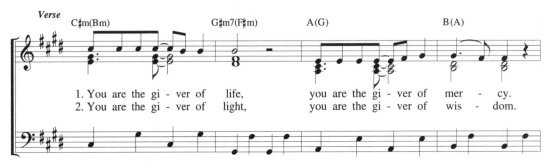

Verse

1. You are the gi - ver of life, you are the gi - ver of mer - cy.
2. You are the gi - ver of light, you are the gi - ver of wis - dom.

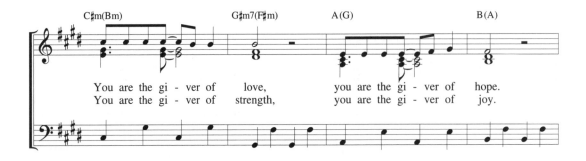

You are the gi - ver of love, you are the gi - ver of hope.
You are the gi - ver of strength, you are the gi - ver of joy.

A CALL TO WORSHIP

(FROM PSALM 95)

The Lord says: come!
Come and sing for joy, offering him your thanks.
Come and recognise his greatness and his glory.
Come and confess him as Maker and Master, Saviour and Security.
We come with glad and eager hearts.

The Lord says: listen!
Listen to the urgency of his invitation;
listen to the tenderness of his warnings;
listen to the greatness of his promises.
We will listen, learn and obey.

You did not consider
(Pouring out)

Nathan Fellingham

1. You did not consider, using all your strength and power to gain yourself an earthly crown;
But instead you suffered, pouring out your life for us to reconcile us back to God.

2. Death could not defeat you. From the grave you rose again, ascending to your Father's side.
Then you sent the Spirit, your pow'r now at work in us to demonstrate your truth and light.

Bridge
What love you showed in doing this for us: my heart it overflows.

So I'm pour-ing out____ a song of love____ and a-dor-a-tion to____ the One____ who's cap-ti-va-ted my____ at-ten-tion: Je-sus Christ,____ the he-ro of____ man-kind's____ sal-va-tion. Thank you, Lord, for this life you've won for me.____

1.,3.

Last time to Coda

112.

You call me in
(Glory streams from your throne)

Worshpfully

Lisa & Wayne Sanders

You call me in, capture my gaze by your grace; how can it be that I can run into the arms of the Almighty One? To your embrace, you see right into my heart; I stand in awe of who you are, and my heart trembles at your majesty.

113.
You find me with one glance
(Glorious life)

Lyrics: Nigel Briggs
Music: Trent

Moderately

1. You find me with one glance,
   gi - ven now I stand; with
2. with me as I wake, I
   you there is no hate. Your

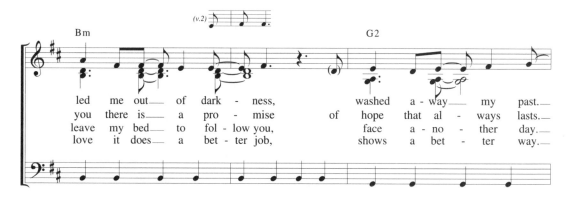

led me out of dark - ness, washed a - way my past.
you there is a pro - mise of hope that al - ways lasts.
leave my bed to fol - low you, face a - no - ther day.
love it does a bet - ter job, shows a bet - ter way.

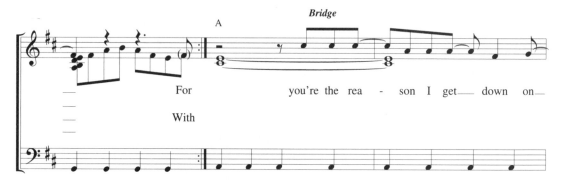

Bridge

For you're the rea - son I get down on
With

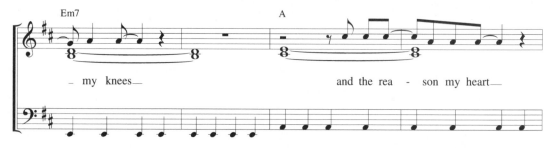

my knees and the rea - son my heart

114. You have shown us

Paul Baloche, Steven Curtis-Chapman, Stuart Garrard,
Israel Houghton, Tim Hughes, Graham Kendrick,
Andy Park, Matt Redman, Martin Smith,
Michael W. Smith, Chris Tomlin, Darlene Zschech

1. You have shown us, O God, what is good.
us the rich-es of your love,

You have shown us, O Lord, what you re-quire.
you have shown us your heart for those in need.

You have heard all our songs, how we
Lord, you're o-pen-ing our ears to the

long to wor-ship you, yet you've taught us the of-f'ring you de-sire.
cries of the poor; you have called us to be your hands and feet.

Chorus

To do just-ly, and to love mer-cy, and to-

115.

You who ride ancient skies above
(Take your place)

Suzanne Hanna

With strength

1. You who ride an-cient skies a-bove,
2. You, who walked the road of suf-fer-ing,

thun - der - ing with mer-cy and with love,
gave your life– a ran-som for our sin.

come and move in this, your dwel - ling place;
Now we stand, a wit-ness to our King;

re - veal your pow - er, glo - ry and your grace. Take your
who was, and is, and will re-turn a - gain.

Your innocence forsaken
(*You Name high*)

116.

Capo 3(D)

Joel Houston

With energy

1. Your in-no-cence for-sa-ken;— up-on that— cross,
2. The at-mos-phere is chang-ing.— oh, can you— hear

you gave your-self for us; car-ried in-to your free-dom.
the peo-ple ris-ing up in— the hope of your free-dom?

Our bro-ken— past re-placed in— a se-cond— chance;
Our for-mer— ways are break-ing.— We seek your— face.

the chains have come un-done. Death— de-fied in the Fa-ther's—
God, let your king-dom come. In— our prai-ses be lift-ed—

Chorus

_ love.— We are li-ving to make— your name high, Je-sus.
_ up.—

we come to-ge-ther. Our one de - sire: to praise you,—

and lift your— up, in our sur-ren-der. 'cause we are

117.

Young and old
(So great)

Capo 3(D)

Steady, building

Paul Baloche, Steven Curtis-Chapman, Stuart Garrard,
Israel Houghton, Tim Hughes, Graham Kendrick,
Andy Park, Matt Redman, Martin Smith,
Michael W. Smith, Chris Tomlin, Darlene Zschech

1. Young and old, rich and poor, weak and strong, ev-'ry-one, come and rest, you are safe in the arms of Je - sus. For he is good, for he is faith - ful. So great, so great,

2. Beau - ti - ful, ma - je - sty, glo - ri - ous, ho - ly One. Rug - ged cross, sov - 'reign grace, oh, the blood of Je - sus.

and your love— en-dures— for e - ver.— To the end— of the age,—

oh, your love— en-dures— for e - ver - more.

ver. So great— - ver - more.

118. Your love

Graham Kendrick
& Dan Wheeler

1. Your love is great-er by far than a-ny love that I have e-ver known; and your love has cap-tured my heart, now I sing with you and I sing for you. Your love reaches to the hea-vens, your love ne-ver

2. Your love will ne-ver let go, and there's no saf-er place than close to you; and your love will never grow cold, so I sing with you and I sing for you.

This song is recorded on the Spring Harvest 'Shine - New Songs 2007' album

ends,— and your love reach - es me;——— and I'm sur -

round - ed by— your good - ness, re - mind - ed of— your mer - cy— dai - ly.

Last time to Coda

Your love reach - es me.

Bridge 1

There has ne - ver been— a great - er love— than this,—

no great - er sa - cri - fice,— no great - er gift.— You

just keep lov-ing us,— oh, who could ask— for more?—— Your

love that seeks— us, saves and keeps— us, there's no

place— your love can't reach us. No great-er,— no high-er.—

(Leader)

Bridge 2

(Response)
There's no place— your love— can't reach— us. No great er,— no high er.—

(Leader)

(Response)
There's no place— your love— can't reach— us. No great er,— no high er.—

(Leader)

APPRENTICED PRAYER

We're apprenticed to a carpenter adept at shaping wood:
Shape our lives, Lord, to your purpose, till we live the way we should.

We're apprenticed to a sculptor who remoulds the twisted soul:
May we share your craft of mercy as you make the wounded whole.

We're apprenticed to a jeweller who is skilled with gems and gold:
May our lives be honed to bear a weight of glory yet untold!

We're apprenticed to a surgeon who can heal the broken heart:
We're astonished by the delicate precision of your art!

© MARTIN E LECKEBUSCH

119. Your mercy taught us how to dance
(Dancing generation)

With energy

Matt Redman

Verse

mer - cy taught us how to dance, to ce - le - brate with
glo - ry taught us how to shout, we'll lift your name in

all we have, and we'll dance to thank you for mer - cy.
all the earth, and we'll shout to the praise of your glo - ry.

1.,3.   2.,4.   *Bridge*

Your   It's the o - ver flow of a for -

gi - ven soul, and now we've seen you, God, our hearts

This song is recorded on the Spring Harvest Live Worship 'One Hope' album

120.

You're calling us
(Call the seeker)

Graham Kendrick
arr. Henry George

Steadily

1. You're call-ing us and so we are ga-thered here; you're
liv-ing stones, built to-ge-ther here with

build-ing us in-to a house of pray'r. A
nail-pierced hands— oh, teach us— ho-ly fear. And

ho-ly place, where sto-ries of grace are told. A sa-cred space where
pray'r will rise for all— na - tions, and o-pen skies will

mi - ra - cles un-fold, and prai - ses rise from the
pour your— glo-ry down and there'll be praise for the

off-'ring of our lives.— Let's fill this house, let's fill— this house.—
Lord is in this place.— Let's fill this house, let's fill— this house.—

Chorus

Call the seek-er, call the stran-ger, call the chil-dren, let's hear their prai-ses.

Call the lone-ly, call the bro-ken; young and old will sing ho-san-nas.

Let's fill this house, let's fill this house with praise.

2. We're

121. You're mighty and strong to save
(Rescuer)

Steadily

Johnny and Cathy Parks
& Nick Herbert

You're migh-ty and strong to save, you're migh-ty and strong to save, you're migh-ty and strong to save, Res-cu-er. You're

From the hea-ven's you came to the depths of the grace to re-
you o-ver-came death it-self for our sake. Let the

deem for your praise: Res-cu-er. Je-sus, er.
world now pro-claim: Res-cu-

303

mi - ghty and— strong to save, Res - cu - er.— You're

er,——— Res - cu - er.

COME HOLY SPIRIT PRAYER

One of the 20th Century pioneers of a charismatic approach to the Christian life was the late John Wimber, founder of the Vineyard movement. From the publication of his first book Power Evangelism onwards, Wimber introduced many Christians to the added dimension brought to faith, life, worship and mission by the dynamic experience of God's Spirit.

And it all began with three small words. For Wimber and those who followed his lead, three simple words of invitation to the third person of the Trinity changed everything: 'Come Holy Spirit'…

So let's take a moment to pray these vital words, and reflect on the areas of our own lives and vision that the coming of the Holy Spirit might revolutionise…

Come Holy Spirit
(Pause)

In the places where we are dry and broken, and have lost the joy of God…
Come Holy Spirit
(Pause)

Where we face obstacles and challenges that are too much for us.
Where our strength is simply not enough to get us through…
Come Holy Spirit
(Pause)

Where those we know and love are struggling.
Where friends and family need to know God's love; to receive his grace; to be transformed by his power…
Come Holy Spirit
(Pause)

Where our cities struggle with the burden of too much sin;
too many questions;
too many false answers.
Where our nations flounder for the loss of their faith…
Come Holy Spirit
(Pause)

**Come Holy Spirit to our families.
Come Holy Spirit to our neighbourhoods and towns.
Come Holy Spirit to our church.
To our homes and hearts: Come Holy Spirit.**

© GERARD KELLY

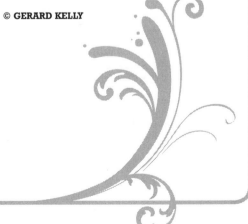

122.
You're the God of this city
(God of this city)

Aaron Boyd, Richard Bleakley, Peter Comfort,
Peter Kernaghan, Andrew McCann & Ian Jordan

Passionately

You're the God of this ci-ty, you're the King of these peo-ple, you're the Lord of this na-tion, you are.

You're the light in this dark-ness, you're the hope to the hope-less, you're the peace to the rest-less, you are.

There is no-one like our God. There is no-one like our God.

There is no - one like⎯ our⎯⎯ God.

LEADING WORSHIP...
WITH CHILDREN!

Jesus said in **Matthew 19, vs 14**, *'Let the children come to me. Don't stop them! For the Kingdom of Heaven belongs to such as these.'*

Ten top tips for leading worship with children

1. Children have a great capacity to worship - they just need to be shown what it is and how to do it. So, teach while you lead. Explain that God loves singing, encourage them to thank God for something good while they sing. Show them how to use their bodies in worship – whether that is having hands raised, bowing down or jumping up in the air!

2. Let them be free! We want our children to have good memories of worship times, so be as celebrational and playful as possible. Encourage them to clap and shout as Psalm 47 says: 'Come on everyone, and clap your hands for joy! Shout to God with joyful praise!' Most of us adults need to remember these words too!

3. Try not to be tokenistic. Too often 'kids songs' are tagged onto a service without much thought. If possible make the all-age time of worship central to the gathering. Encourage the whole church to participate – that might mean politely asking the adults at the back to stand and join in!

4. Pick songs that children can relate to and sing easily. Catchy melodies and simple lyrics will help them to join in and feel part of the action.

5. Don't be afraid of also including more adult-focused songs in family times of worship. Many of our contemporary worship songs are very accessible to children and it's good to be inclusive in both directions! This can help to bridge the gap between the young and old in the church.

6. Actions are great! In fact, they help children learn the songs more quickly. Ideally, have some 'action leaders' up front – either a couple of adults (to make the point that this is for everyone!) or it could also be a good chance to involve some of the older children by getting them to lead up front.

7. Think about the theology of the songs you're using as it's the songs, rather than any teaching, that children will predominantly remember. Try and pick a broad range of songs that will reveal God in different ways, as Father, friend, creator, the one who answers prayers, the one who forgives.

8. Think of the child when choosing songs and planning how to lead. Children love to have fun so find songs that are upbeat and silly and reflect the joy of praising God. Children also know what it feels like to suffer – whether that's due to bullying, family breakdown or illness, so find songs that will connect with struggles a child might be having, and remind them of God's great love and presence with them. This will help sustain them through the week.

9. Communicate with your children's worker or Sunday school helpers. Try and be joined up so that there's some continuity in what the children are singing about and learning about in their groups. It may work to use the all-age time of worship as a chance for some children to share what God's been doing in their lives or for a child to pray.

10. Finally, remember that you are part of something very special and significant when you lead children into the presence of their Father. You're building the future church! So, find the child within you and enjoy it!

Nick & Becky Drake

Nick & Becky Drake
Big Family of God CD

Available from all good Christian retailers, iTunes & EssentialChristian.com

ALL AGE WORSHIP

Well, sooner or later many of us will be sucked into and involved in all age worship in our church. Many people fear this day, and would rather have their eyebrows shaved off than be involved. But guess what? All age worship can be amazing. All age worship can be fun! All age worship can and should gather together the church family to worship our Big God. So here are 10 top tips in leading all age worship whether you're playing a guitar or the spoons, aged 80 or 8 or whether you waiting for your eyebrows to grow back! So here are a few tips that may be helpful in your celebration. These are not perfect but may be enough to save your eyebrows!

ONE – Think fresh!

There's nothing quite like hearing a new song on the radio that makes you want to tap the gear leaver in the car while you're driving. We all like new fresh things. So let's work on keeping our all age worship fresh. Don't keep hold of things because they have 'always been'. Step out and try something new. How about introduce a kid's choir, some new musicians,

TWO – Think Big!

One of the things I love doing is thinking big. Why not! If people never thought big, would we have the Telephone, hydrogen cars or a Microwave? Don't be limited to what's always been. Even with a small modest budget you can make a hall or stage look great. Buy some balloons, t-shirts for the team or what about some yummy muffins instead of the old rich tea biscuits!

THREE – Be totally inclusive

I love cola bottle sweets. But I know if I had a whole bag of them, not only would I be ill but also get bored of the same. That's why I get some of those yummy pink shrimp ones too! Don't just aim it at one area of church. Try and include everyone! Don't have 'special slots' for the kids, or for the adults, but mix it all together. Design the celebration to flow from song to song and activity to activity. This shows that everyone is valued, important and can worship together.

FOUR – Have fun

Have fun and be seen having fun. Be enthusiastic about the worship, in fact the whole event. Get enthusiastic. Be demonstrative in the worship. This will not only inspire others but will encourage kids to follow your leading. Many churches rarely have the whole church together in a service - so make it a real celebration as a church family. And don't forget to smile!

FIVE - Be Creative

Why not make a small stage set, hire some lights, buy some balloons, stick a logo on the kick drum, or introduce some 'characters' into your celebration. You could encourage some of you kids and youth to join with the band. Why not put together a kids/youth choir. Why not mix the service up –you don't have to stick to the usual format! If you have computers and projectors - buy some new movie backgrounds for the songs. Think creative and think big!

SIX - Be honourable

Have as much fun as you can with every one – but don't forget those that might find the celebration difficult. Ensure they feel included whether by leading something, being on a team or maybe having a place as part of the worship or service. Try not to alienate anyone - so if that means doing a hymn - that's cool - do it fun and well. Let's strive to make all age worship not just inclusive but also a time that honours those for whom this may take time to adjust.

SEVEN - Make it accessible

Don't forget everyone. There will be people of all ages - so try and choose songs that people not only know but are able to worship too. This might be a great time to teach a new song - or highlight a song that the children love to worship with, Try and mix up well loved and known kids and adult songs in the sets.

EIGHT - Make it interactive

There's nothing worse than watching paint dry, well apart from eyebrows growing back! So don't just sing and speak to the congregation – include them! Get them involved in the worship; get them to respond in the worship, sketches, talks and games. Invite members up to take part. Have interviews or pre film clips with people from the congregation. Why not have a couple of people host the celebration.

NINE - Don't be afraid to lead

I don't like getting lost and I don't get on with maps. So, on most journeys, my wife will use the map and tell me where to turn. Without her leading me in the car, who knows where we might end up. It's the same in all age worship. Be prepared to lead. Direct and encourage the church. 'Let's stand', 'let's all raise our hands', 'let's all sing out' are simple directions that might make a huge difference in the worship. Children will also find that easy to follow and enable them to join in with everyone else.

TEN - Rock the place!

Yeah! Have a great time in worship. Yes, if you are blessed with musicians and full bands – use them. Put together a kid's choir, have people lead dance on the stage, make space for the congregation to move or even, brace yourself – dance! Worship God is one of the best things we can do, so let's take people with us on that journey of fun, joy and adoration to our living God.

Simon Parry

Simon Parry
God's Love is Big CD

Available from all good Christian retailers, iTunes & EssentialChristian.com

CHOOSING A GUITAR...
FOR WORSHIP

So, you've got the money, you've saved and sold every domestic use item in the house to gain the funds, you've even got permission from the other half/parents/partner/domestic pet (one has to be all inclusive on these things!). You go heart racing to the music store to find that one guitar that will make you feel a million dollars when you play; that one guitar that will shake the very foundations of music itself. But you get there and the guitar dream juggernaut comes shuddering to a halt!...which one do I pick?...there's so many!.. and so many different shapes....fear not Dr Danny B has a few words of simple advice to help keep the Guitar indigestion at bay!!

We all have that one sound in our heads as guitar players whether a beginner or old hand that we want to hear or sound like. What I mention here will be broad brush and meant only as a helpful starting point but, at Taylor Guitars we always say the best place to start is with the shape of the guitar together with your personal playing style.

Different guitar shapes obviously have different sounds! A smaller body acoustic for instance (like a Grand Concert, 0/00 size) with a narrower waist and less body depth will be great for a fingerstyle/ light strummer. Good for studio and live, it controls the boomier sound and overtones you sometimes get in bigger bodied guitars. The overall effect being that it doesn't fight sonically with other instruments on stage or in the studio. Due to their size and depth these can sometimes be a quieter guitar and may have a shorter scale neck which means the strings are often a little slinkier and easier on the hands to play.

A larger body guitar (like a Jumbo, Dreadnought or Grand Symphony) will have a much stronger bass and lower midrange response and be perfect for those who play with picks and like to give the guitar some welly! This makes them great for live and in the case of a Jumbo or a 12 string there is lots of volume, a robust low end and depth to the overall tone.

Often a guitar which sits in the middle of these two styles in size and shape will be a great all rounder a kind of Swiss Army knife of guitars (a Grand Auditorium or M/000 size are good examples) these will work really well for someone who wants something for all occasions but maybe isn't quite as 'specialist' in sound as other shapes.

I could go on we could talk about the effect of different tone woods on the back and sides of a guitar the effect of the sound board and pickup systems! (Did I see rolling of eyes?). But hopefully this will give you a really brief and helpful intro into picking an acoustic guitar for yourself. Ultimately, get out to the shops, try as many as you can and remember that the wood, the body and your style all impact the sound. Happy playing!

Dan Boreham
Taylor Guitars European Product Specialist

GUITAR CHORDS

A good chord vocabulary is essential for a guitarist to feel confident when playing in worship, especially when the situation may involve reading a previously unseen piece of music or picking up a song quickly by ear. The chords on these pages are arranged in 'families' according to key. This is a beneficial way of remembering chords as most songs stick to these groupings. For each key, the first row shows the simplest form of each chord and the second line gives a more interesting substitution. The third line shows the chords most commonly used by guitarists derived by keeping some sort of pedal tone ringing in each chord and the fourth line shows inverted chords with an alternate bass note.

Also included are the Roman Numerals and Nashville Numbers associated with each chord. If you've not come across these before, they are simply an easy way of numbering each chord within a key. This is useful as it means you can take any chord progression in one key and instantly transpose it to another. Furthermore you can try out any of the chords in each column that corresponds to the relevant Roman Numeral and see if there is chord type or inversion which still fits but adds a different flavour. Experimentation like this may open up creative chord progressions that serve as a catalyst to help you to worship in fresh ways or to write new songs.

Roman	I	II	III	IV	V	VI	VII
Nashville	1	2	3	4	5	6	7
3-note chord (triad)	C	Dm	Em	F	G	Am	Bdim
4-note chord	Cmaj7	Dm7	Em7	Fmaj7	G7	Am7	Bm7♭5
Alternative substitute	C	D7sus4	Em7	Fsus2	G5	Am7	Dsus4/B
Alternative bass note	C/E	Dm/F	Em/G	F/A	F/G	Am/E	

(Key of C)

For all chords in the key of C# or Db, use the chords from the key of C with capo 1

More Chord Charts Overleaf

313

GUITAR CHORDS

	Roman	I	II	III	IV	V	VI	VII
	Nashville	1	2	3	4	5	6	7
Key of D	3-note chord (triad)	D	Em	F#m	G	A	Bm	C#dim
	4-note chord	Dmaj7	Em7	F#m7	Gmaj7	A7	Bm7	C#m7♭5
	Alternative substitute	Dsus2	Em9	F#m7	G6sus2	A7sus4	Bm11	Aadd9/C#
	Alternative bass note	D/F#	Em/B	F#m/A	G/B	G/A	Bm/F#	

For all chords in the key of D# or E♭, use the chords from the key of D with capo 1

	Roman	I	II	III	IV	V	VI	VII
Key of E	3-note chord (triad)	E	F#m	G#m	A	B	C#m	D#dim
	4-note chord	Emaj7	F#m7	G#m7	Amaj7	B7	C#m7	D#m7♭5
	Alternative substitute	E5	F#m11	G#madd♭6	Aadd9	Badd4	C#m7	D#alt
	Alternative bass note	E/G#	F#m/C#	G#m/D#	A/C#	A/B	C#m/G#	

For all chords in the key of F, use the chords from the key of E with capo 1

For all chords in the key of F# or Gb, use the chords from the key of E with capo 2

314

GUITAR CHORDS

	Roman	I	II	III	IV	V	VI	VII
	Nashville	1	2	3	4	5	6	7
Key of G	3-note chord (triad)	G	Am	Bm	C	D	Em	F#dim
	4-note chord	G maj7	A m7	B m7	C maj7	D7	E m7	F#m7♭5
	Alternative substitute	G	A 7sus4	D sus4/B	C add9	D sus4	E m7	G/F#
	Alternative bass note	G/D	A m/C	B m/D	C/G	C/D	Em/G	
	For all chords in the key of G# or A♭, use the chords from the key of G with capo 1							
Key of A	3-note chord (Triad)	A	Bm	C#m	D	E	F#m	G#dim
	4-note chord	A maj7	B m7	C#m7	D maj7	E7	F#m7	G#m7♭5
	Alternative substitute	A sus2	B sus4	C#m7	D6sus2	E add9	F#m11	E add9/G#
	Alternative bass note	A/E	Bm/F#	C#m/E	D/A	D/E	F#m/A	

For all chords in the key of A# or Bb, use the chords from the key of A with capo 1

For all chords in the key of B, use the chords from the key of A with capo 2

Richard Stephenson & Andy Flannagan

SCRIPTURE INDEX

MICAH

6:8	Forth In Your Name
6:8	Hear the call of the kingdom
6:8	You Have Shown Us

NAHUM

| 1:7 | Amazing grace |

HABAKKUK

| 1:12 | Everlasting |

ZEPHANIAH

3:16	You're Mighty And Strong To Save
3:17	Everyone needs compassion
3:17	Looking In The Sky

ZECHARIAH

| 2:10 | Dance, dance |
| 13:9 | This Is My Prayer In The Desert |

MALACHI

| 3:3 | This Is My Prayer In The Desert |

MATTHEW

5:16	In All I Do And All I Say
5:3-14	Blessed Are You
6:10	Spirit Of God
6:10	We wait in hope for you
6:10	We Your Children Pray Lord
6:10	We're Living For Your Presence Lord
6:13	O Sovereign God
9:38	How Shall They Hear Who Have Not Heard
11:5	Christ Is The One Who Calls
11:28	Forth In Your Name
11:16-19	O Christ The Same, Through All Our Story's Pages
11:25-30	O Christ The Same, Through All Our Story's Pages
12:22	When I call on your name
16:18	Let Voices Sing, Let Anthems Rise
17:20	Everyone needs compassion
20:1	Forth In Your Name
20:28	You who ride ancient skies above
21:9	I See The King Of Glory
21:9	Praise is rising, eyes are turning to you
21:15	I See The King Of Glory
21:15	Praise is rising, eyes are turning to you
24:14	How Shall They Hear Who Have Not Heard
24:30-31	This Joyful Eastertide
25:27-31	Sweet Jesus Christ, My Sanity
26:41	Forth In Your Name
26:26-28	He Became Sin
26:26-28	Sweet Jesus Christ, My Sanity
26:26-28	This Is The Body Of Christ
27:51	O Lord you've searched me
28:6	Christ Is The One Who Calls
28:6	See, what a morning
28:19	In the name of the Father

MARK

10:31	We're Taller When We Bow
10:45	You who ride ancient skies above
11:9-10	I See The King Of Glory
11:9-10	Praise is rising, eyes are turning to you
13:10	How Shall They Hear Who Have Not Heard
13:33	Forth In Your Name
14:38	Forth In Your Name

14:22-24	He Became Sin
14:22-24	Sweet Jesus Christ, My Sanity
14:22-24	This Is The Body Of Christ
15:38	O Lord you've searched me
16:6	See, what a morning
16:14	My Life Is Built On Your Promises

LUKE

1:78	At The Start, He Was There
4:18-19	Mercy to the broken hearted
5:5	Forth In Your Name
6:20-22	Blessed Are You
7:22	Christ Is The One Who Calls
11:2	Spirit Of God
11:2	We wait in hope for you
11:2	We Your Children Pray Lord
11:2	We're Living For Your Presence Lord
15:6	Amazing grace
15:24	Amazing grace
15:24	How Do I Ever Thank You
15:32	Dance, dance
15:32	How Do I Ever Thank You
19:10	Christ Is The One Who Calls
19:10	Shout the news that God is here
19:38	All I Have And All I Am Is Yours
21:36	Forth In Your Name
22:42	I Stand Amazed
23:45	O Lord you've searched me
24:6	Christ Is The One Who Calls
24:6	See, what a morning
24:23	The greatest day in history
24:34	My Life Is Built On Your Promises
24:14-20	He Became Sin
24:14-20	Sweet Jesus Christ, My Sanity
24:14-20	This Is The Body Of Christ

JOHN

1:5	A Thousand Times
1:5	You're The God Of This City
1:14	At The Start, He Was There
1:20	We Bow Our Hearts
1:36	We Bow Our Hearts
4:10	Lord of the church
8:12	Light of the world
8:31	Father, My Heart Belongs To You
9:1	Amazing grace
9:36	Let all, all thanksgiving
11:25	On The Darkest Day Of All
11:27	Let all, all thanksgiving
12:13	I See The King Of Glory
12:13	Praise is rising, eyes are turning to you
12:36	Hear the call of the kingdom
14:3	Sweet Jesus Christ, My Sanity
14:5-7	Christ The Eternal Lord
15:13	Your love
16:30	Let all, all thanksgiving
17:11	Lord of the church
17:18	How Shall They Hear Who Have Not Heard
20:9	See, what a morning
20:21	How Shall They Hear Who Have Not Heard

ACTS

2:1	Lord of the church
2:25	Forth In Your Name
10:36	He Became Sin
18:9	Your mercy taught us how to dance
20:24	Forth In Your Name

ROMANS

1:6	Life Could Take
1:20	Before The First
119-20	Looking In The Sky
5:8	Looking In The Sky
5:1-2	Before The First
5:8-10	Christ The Eternal Lord
6:10	Once For All
6:10	The greatest day in history
6:4-11	On The Darkest Day Of All
8:1	When I'm Weak
8:11	On The Darkest Day Of All
8:26	Jesus You Are Here With Us
8:34	My Life Is Built On Your Promises
8:38-39	Giver of life, you never change
9:5	For every song, for every breath
9:5	Lord of the church
10:12	He Became Sin
10:12	Lord of the church
10:14	How Shall They Hear Who Have Not Heard
11:20	Be Still And Know
11:36	All I Have And All I Am Is Yours
11:5-6	I Was Lost When You Found Me Here
12:1	Take My Life
12:2	Forth In Your Name
15:6	Give Unto The Lord

1 CORINTHIANS

1:18	Veiled in humanness
1:26	We're Taller When We Bow
1:30	At The Start, He Was There
1:30	When I'm Weak
2:3	Forth In Your Name
2:6	You who ride ancient skies above
2:9	Wonderful, so wonderful
3:8	Let Voices Sing, Let Anthems Rise
3:10	Everlasting God
3:11	If ever I should falter
6:11	In the shadow of the cross
9:24	We Bow Our Hearts
11:24-25	He Became Sin
11:24-25	Sweet Jesus Christ, My Sanity
11:24-25	This Is The Body Of Christ
13:12	Christ The Eternal Lord
13:4-7	Giver of life, you never change
15:3	Your Innocence Forsaken
15:3	Lord, I lift your name on high
15:14	This Joyful Eastertide
15:20	My Life Is Built On Your Promises
15:20	Sweet Jesus Christ, My Sanity
15:26	All Creatures Of Our God And King
15:52	Bring Heaven To Earth, Lord
15:52	This Joyful Eastertide
15:54	O precious sight, my Saviour stands
15:54	The greatest day in history
15:55	Veiled in humanness
15:55-56	Christ Is The One Who Calls

2 CORINTHIANS

1:12	This is how I know what love is
4:16	Forth In Your Name
12:8-10	When I'm Weak
13:4	Veiled in humanness

EPHESIANS

1:20	On The Darkest Day Of All
1:21	For every song, for every breath
1:21	Let Voices Sing, Let Anthems Rise
1:23	You Are A Great God
2:5	Amazing grace
2:8	Amazing grace
2:8	I Was Lost When You Found Me Here
2:16	Veiled in humanness
2:22	You who ride ancient skies above
3:10	Let Voices Sing, Let Anthems Rise
3:19	Love That Will Not Let Me Go
4:32	All Creatures Of Our God And King
4:4-6	For every song, for every breath
5:1	Hear the call of the kingdom

PHILIPPIANS

2:8	Light of the world
2:9	Jesus, there is no one like you
2:9	O Sovereign God
2:9	There's a song that's rising up inside
2:9	Worship The Lord
2:10	Spirit Of God
2:10	Your Innocence Forsaken
2:10-11	There Is A Song
2:10-11	We're Living For Your Presence Lord
2:6-11	You Did Not Consider
2:8-9	Christ Is The One Who Calls
2:8-9	He Became Sin
3:10	All I Am I Lay It Down
3:10	All I Have And All I Am
3:10	All I Have And All I Am Is Yours
3:10	Jesus, my passion in life
3:14	If ever I should falter
3:14	We Bow Our Hearts
3:14	We're Taller When We Bow
4:6	How Do I Ever Thank You

COLOSSIANS

1:10	Bring Heaven To Earth, Lord
1:18	God in my living
1:20	Veiled in humanness
1:22	O precious sight, my Saviour stands
1:27	There Is A Song
1:29	On The Darkest Day Of All
1:11-28	O Christ The Same, Through All Our Story's Pages
3:12	Life Could Take
3:17	In All I Do And All I Say
4:2	Forth In Your Name

1 THESSALONIANS

1:4	Life Could Take
4:14	Let all, all thanksgiving
4:16	This Joyful Eastertide
5:5	Hear the call of the kingdom
5:8	We Your Children Pray Lord

319

THEMATIC INDEX

CALL TO WORSHIP

All creation is a song
Dance, dance
Give unto the Lord
Hear the call of the kingdom
In the name of the Father
Let all, all thanksgiving
Let voices sing, let anthems rise
Lord of the church
Praise awaits for thee
Praise is rising
Praise the Lord from the heavens
Shout the news that God is here
Sing unto the Lord a new song
Strength will rise
There's a song that's rising up inside
We bow our hearts
We could try to count the stars
We will sing, sing, sing
Worship the Lord
Would you restore the place I hold for you
You are a great God
You call me in
Young and old
You're calling us

CHURCH: ONE PEOPLE

All creation is a song
Hear the call of the kingdom
In the name of the Father
Jesus you are here with us
Let voices sing, let anthems rise
Lord of the church
Lord, you are good
Loved before the dawn of time
Oh God we're crying out to you
Our God will reign forever
There is a song
We your children pray Lord
Your innocence forsaken
You're calling us

COME LORD JESUS - THE PRESENCE OF GOD

Bring heaven to earth, Lord
Everyone needs compassion
Father, my heart belongs to you
God in my living
Jesus Christ, you never change
Jesus you are here with us
Jesus, my passion in life
Lord of the church
Love that will not let me go
Mercy to the broken-hearted
My life is built on your promises
O Lord you've searched me
Oh God we're crying out to you
Praise is rising
Shout the news that God is here
Spirit of God
Strength will rise

We wait in hope for you
We your children pray Lord
We're living for your presence Lord
When I'm lost
You who ride ancient skies above

COMMUNION
(SEE ALSO JESUS - CROSS AND RESURRECTION)

He became sin
In the shadow of the cross
Life could take
Light of the world
O Lord you've searched me
O precious sight
On the darkest day of all
Sweet Jesus Christ, my sanity
This is the body of Christ
Veiled in humanness

CONFESSION

A thousand times
Everyone needs compassion
I stand amazed
I was lost when you found me here
If ever I should falter
Loved before the dawn of time
My times are in your hands
O Lord you've searched me
Spirit of God
This is my prayer in the desert
To you O Lord
We your children pray Lord
When I'm lost
When I'm weak
Would you restore the place I hold for you

CREATION

All creation is a song
All creatures of our God and King
Be still and know
Before the first
Everlasting, ever true
God of the mountains
Great is the Lord and most worthy of praise
In the beginning was darkness
Looking in the sky
Praise the Lord from the heavens
We could try to count the stars
When I see the beauty

DEDICATION AND COMMITMENT

A thousand times
All I am, I lay it down
All I have and all I am
Everlasting, ever true
Everyone needs compassion
Father, my heart belongs to you
Forth in your Name
Great are you Lord

Hear the call of the kingdom
Heaven's King
High in the heavens
'How shall they hear', who have not heard
I see the King of glory
If ever I should falter
In all I do and all I say
Jesus Christ, you never change
Let voices sing, let anthems rise
Loved before the dawn of time
Spirit of God
Take my life
This is my prayer in the desert
Though trials will come
We're living for your presence Lord
We're taller when we bow
When I see the beauty
When we were in the darkest night
Who am I
Worship the Lord
You did not consider
You have shown us
Your innocence forsaken

FAITH AND TRUST

Amazing grace
Be still and know
Christ the eternal Lord
Everlasting God
God in my living
Great are you Lord
Heaven's King
In all glory
I've had questions
Let voices sing, let anthems rise
My life is built on your promises
My times are in your hands
Rock of ages
Strength will rise
The greatest day in history
This is my prayer in the desert
Though trials will come
To you O Lord
We have a strong and certain hope
We wait in hope for you
When clouds veil sun
When I call on your name
When we were in the darkest night

FAMILY WORSHIP

Dance, dance
I offer up to you
Lord, I lift your name on high
Sing unto the Lord a new song
The greatest day in history
There's a song that's rising up inside
We will sing, sing, sing
Who am I
You are a great God
Young and old
Your mercy taught us how to dance

GOD, LORD AND FATHER

All I am, I lay it down
Everlasting God
Father, my heart belongs to you
Give unto the Lord
God of the mountains
In all glory
Lord, you are good
Love that will not let me go
Praise the Lord from the heavens
Rock of ages
Shout the news that God is here
Sing unto the Lord a new song
Strength will rise
Though trials will come
To you O Lord
We could try to count the stars
We wait in hope for you
We're taller when we bow
When clouds veil sun
You are a great God

GOD'S LOVE AND FAITHFULNESS

Amazing grace
At the start, he was there
Dance, dance
Giver of life
He became sin
I see the King of glory
I stand amazed
I was lost when you found me here
If ever I should falter
In all I do and all I say
In the shadow of the cross
Life could take
Loved before the dawn of time
My soul will sing
O Lord you've searched me
O precious sight
Once for all
There is a song
This joyful Eastertide
To you O Lord
We have a strong and certain hope
We your children pray Lord
When I call on your name
When I'm weak
When we were in the darkest night
Who am I
You find me with one glance
You who ride ancient skies above
Young and old
Your love

GUIDANCE AND DIRECTION

All I am, I lay it down
All I have and all I am is yours
Forth in your Name
My times are in your hands
Rock of ages
Take my life
Though trials will come
To you O Lord
We wait in hope for you

We will sing, sing, sing
When we were in the darkest night
Would you restore the place I hold
for you
You have shown us

HEALING

Before the first
Christ is the one who calls
God in my living
I see the King of glory
I've had questions
Lord of the church
Mercy to the broken-hearted
O Sovereign God
Strength will rise
There's a name I love to hear
This is my prayer in the desert
We your children pray Lord

HEART WORSHIP

All I have and all I am
Amazing grace
Dance, dance
Everlasting, ever true
Father, my heart belongs to you
For every song
Give unto the Lord
Hallelujah
How do I ever thank you
I offer up to you
In all I do and all I say
I've had questions
Jesus Christ, you never change
Jesus, my passion in life
Jesus, there is no one like You
Life could take
Light of the world
My soul will sing
O precious sight
Sing unto the Lord a new song
Spirit of God
Take my life
The greatest day in history
There's a name I love to hear
There's a song that's rising up inside
This is how I know what love is
We bow our hearts
We could try to count the stars
We will sing, sing, sing
We're taller when we bow
When I call on your name
When I'm lost
Wonderful, so wonderful
Worship the Lord
You call me in
You did not consider
Your love
Your mercy taught us how to dance

HEAVEN AND THE PROMISE OF ETERNITY: ONE HOPE

Amazing grace
Christ the eternal Lord
Forth in your Name
I stand amazed

Jesus Christ, you never change
O Christ the same
O Lord you've searched me
On the darkest day of all
Rock of ages
The greatest day in history

HOLY SPIRIT

High in the heavens
How do I ever thank you
'How shall they hear', who have not
heard
In the beginning was darkness
Let voices sing, let anthems rise
Oh God we're crying out to you
Spirit of God
You did not consider

JESUS - CROSS AND RESURRECTION

Amazing grace
At the start, he was there
Before the first
Christ is the one who calls
Everyone needs compassion
He became sin
How do I ever thank you
Jesus Christ, you never change
Life could take
Light of the world
Lord, I lift your name on high
Loved before the dawn of time
My life is built on your promises
O Lord you've searched me
O precious sight
On the darkest day of all
Once for all
Our God will reign forever
See what a morning
Sweet Jesus Christ, my sanity
The greatest day in history
This is how I know what love is
This joyful Eastertide
We have a strong and certain hope
When I call on your name
When I see the beauty
You did not consider
Your innocence forsaken
You're mighty and strong to save

JUSTICE

Blessed are you who are poor
Bring heaven to earth, Lord
Let voices sing, let anthems rise
My soul will sing
Shout the news that God is here
Spirit of God
Strength will rise
We're living for your presence Lord
You have shown us
You're the God of this city

LOVE AND DEVOTION

All I have and all I am
Father, my heart belongs to you
Give unto the Lord
Great are you Lord

Hallelujah
I offer up to you
In all glory
Jesus Christ, you never change
Jesus, my passion in life
Let all, all thanksgiving
Light of the world
Looking in the sky
Love that will not let me go
Our God will reign forever
Sing unto the Lord a new song
Spirit of God
Take my life
There's a song that's rising up inside
We bow our hearts
We could try to count the stars
We will sing, sing, sing
Wonderful, so wonderful
Worship the Lord
You call me in
You did not consider
Your mercy taught us how to dance

MERCY, GRACE AND FORGIVENESS

A thousand times
All I am, I lay it down
Amazing grace
At the start, he was there
Dance, dance
Everyone needs compassion
Giver of life
He became sin
I see the King of glory
I stand amazed
I was lost when you found me here
If ever I should falter
In the shadow of the cross
Jesus, there is no one like You
Life could take
Looking in the sky
Lord, you are good
Loved before the dawn of time
Mercy to the broken-hearted
My soul will sing
O Christ the same
O precious sight
Once for all
Sweet Jesus Christ, my sanity
The greatest day in history
There is a song
This is how I know what love is
When I call on your name
When I'm lost
When I'm weak
Would you restore the place I hold for you
You find me with one glance
Your love
Your mercy taught us how to dance
You're mighty and strong to save

MISSION

Blessed are you who are poor
Bring heaven to earth, Lord
Christ is the one who calls
Christ the eternal Lord

Forth in your Name
Great are you Lord
Hear the call of the kingdom
'How shall they hear', who have not heard
In all I do and all I say
Let voices sing, let anthems rise
Shout the news that God is here
Spirit of God
There is a song
This is how I know what love is
We're living for your presence Lord
You have shown us
You're calling us
You're the God of this city

MYSTERY/ TRANSCENDENCE AND POWER OF GOD

Amazing grace
At the start, he was there
Be still and know
Before the first
Christ the eternal Lord
Everlasting God
For every song
God of the mountains
Great is the Lord and most worthy of praise
Let all, all thanksgiving
O Christ the same
Praise the Lord from the heavens
We could try to count the stars
When we were in the darkest night
Worship the Lord
You are a great God
You call me in
You who ride ancient skies above

PRAISE AND THANKSGIVING

A thousand times
All creatures of our God and King
Christ the eternal Lord
Dance, dance
Everlasting, ever true
Give unto the Lord
Great are you Lord
Great is the Lord and most worthy of praise
Hallelujah
I offer up to you
I stand amazed
In all glory
In the shadow of the cross
Jesus, there is no one like You
Let all, all thanksgiving
Light of the world
Lord of the church
Lord, I lift your name on high
Loved before the dawn of time
My soul will sing
O Christ the same
O Sovereign God
Our God will reign forever
Praise awaits for thee
Praise is rising

Praise the Lord from the heavens
Sing unto the Lord a new song
The greatest day in history
There's a song that's rising up inside
This is how I know what love is
This is my prayer in the desert
We bow our hearts
We could try to count the stars
We will sing, sing, sing
We're living for your presence Lord
When I call on your name
When I see the beauty
When we were in the darkest night
Wonderful, so wonderful
You are a great God
You find me with one glance
Your innocence forsaken
Your mercy taught us how to dance
You're mighty and strong to save

PRAYER AND INTERCESSION

All I have and all I am is yours
Bring heaven to earth, Lord
Father, my heart belongs to you
God in my living
How do I ever thank you
I see the King of glory
Jesus you are here with us
Jesus, my passion in life
Lord of the church
Oh God we're crying out to you
Spirit of God
This is my prayer in the desert
We your children pray Lord
We're living for your presence Lord
You're calling us

PROCLAMATION

All creation is a song
Before the first
Christ is the one who calls
Everlasting God
Everyone needs compassion
For every song
Give unto the Lord
Giver of life
High in the heavens
In all glory
In the name of the Father
Let all, all thanksgiving
Let voices sing, let anthems rise
Lord, you are good
Once for all
Our God will reign forever
Rock of ages
Shout the news that God is here
Strength will rise
There is a song
There's a name I love to hear
We have a strong and certain hope
We will sing, sing, sing
When clouds veil sun
When I'm weak
Wonderful, so wonderful
You are a great God
You're mighty and strong to save
You're the God of this city

RENEWAL AND REFRESHMENT

Amazing grace
At the start, he was there
Father, my heart belongs to you
How do I ever thank you
I was lost when you found me here
If ever I should falter
In the beginning was darkness
Love that will not let me go
Mercy to the broken-hearted
My life is built on your promises
O Lord you've searched me
O Sovereign God
Praise is rising
Strength will rise
Take my life
Though trials will come
To you O Lord
We your children pray Lord
We're taller when we bow
When I'm lost
When I'm weak
Would you restore the place I hold for you
Young and old

RESPONSE

A thousand times
All I am, I lay it down
All I have and all I am
Blessed are you who are poor
Father, my heart belongs to you
Forth in your Name
God in my living
Great are you Lord
Hear the call of the kingdom
Heaven's King
How do I ever thank you
'How shall they hear', who have not heard
I offer up to you
I stand amazed
I've had questions
Jesus you are here with us
Life could take

Light of the world
My soul will sing
My times are in your hands
O Christ the same
O precious sight
Oh God we're crying out to you
Rock of ages
Spirit of God
Take my life
There's a song that's rising up inside
This is my prayer in the desert
We bow our hearts
We could try to count the stars
We your children pray Lord
We're living for your presence Lord
We're taller when we bow
When we were in the darkest night
Worship the Lord
Would you restore the place I hold for you
You did not consider
You have shown us
Your innocence forsaken

SPIRITUAL WARFARE

Hallelujah
If ever I should falter
In all glory
Jesus you are here with us
Let all, all thanksgiving
O Sovereign God
Once for all
Shout the news that God is here
There's a name I love to hear
This is my prayer in the desert
Though trials will come
You're mighty and strong to save
You're the God of this city

SUFFERING AND TRIALS

All creatures of our God and King
Blessed are you who are poor
Giver of life
God in my living
I was lost when you found me here
If ever I should falter

I've had questions
Let all, all thanksgiving
Life could take
Love that will not let me go
My times are in your hands
O Sovereign God
Praise is rising
Strength will rise
This is my prayer in the desert
Though trials will come
We wait in hope for you
When clouds veil sun
When I'm weak
When we were in the darkest night
You who ride ancient skies above

SUITABLE FOR SOLO OR PRESENTATION

At the start, he was there
Bring heaven to earth, Lord
God in my living
Jesus you are here with us
Love that will not let me go
O precious sight
Take my life
This is my prayer in the desert
We wait in hope for you
We your children pray Lord
We're taller when we bow
When clouds veil sun
Would you restore the place I hold for you
You call me in
You have shown us
Young and old

TRINITY

All creatures of our God and King
Great is the Lord and most worthy of praise
In the name of the Father
Let all, all thanksgiving
O Sovereign God
See what a morning

SPOKEN WORSHIP INDEX

MUSICIAN'S NOTEPAD

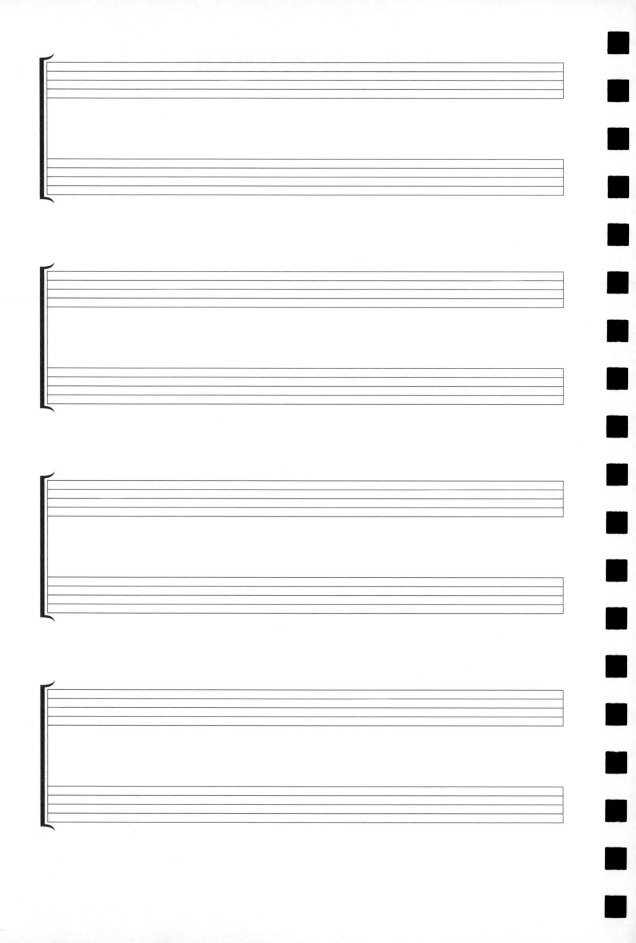

MUSICIAN'S NOTEPAD